SCHOOLS COUNCIL

MODULAR COURSES IN TECH

INSTRUMENTATION

Malcolm Plant

Dr Jan Stuart

Oliver & Boyd

in association with the National Centre for School Technology

PROJECT TEAM

Director
Dr Ray Page

Co-ordinators
Roy Pickup
John Poole

Jeffrey Hall
Dr Duncan Harris
John Hucker
Michael Ive
Peter Patient

Oliver & Boyd

Robert Stevenson House
1 — 3 Baxter's Place
Leith Walk
Edinburgh EH1 3BB

A Division of Longman Group UK Ltd

First published 1983
Third impression 1986
© SCDC Publications 1983

Produced by Longman Group (FE) Ltd
Printed in Hong Kong

ISBN 0-05-003544-4

Contents

Acknowledgements

For permission to reproduce certain photographs in this book, the authors and publishers would like to thank the following:

NASA (Figs. 1.1 and 1.18);
Avo Ltd, Dover, England (Fig. 1.5);
Comark Electronics Ltd (Fig. 2.3);
A. Gallenkamp & Co. Ltd (Fig. 5.1);
Casio Electronics Co. Ltd (Figs. 5.2 and 5.4);
Weston Instruments (Fig. 7.1);
Computer Engineering Ltd (Fig. 8.2);
Picker International Ltd (Fig. 10.1);
TI Raleigh Ltd (Fig. 12.1);
Tony Nash (Fig. 13.1).

Note The sign ■ has been used in the text to signify the basic course material. The sign □ indicates the more advanced sections.

1 Making Measurements

■ Sizing Up Life

Have you ever stopped to think how very interested we all are in knowing how hot, bright, tall, long, cold, strong things are? This natural urge to 'size up' the world in which we live must be the reason why the *Guinness Book of Records* makes such fascinating reading. For example:

> Did you know that a man has been able to lift a **weight** equal to the weight of thirty-five average men?
>
> Did you know that an unclothed man has endured a dry-air **temperature** of 200°C? (Water boils at 100°C at sea level and a steak can be cooked at 160°C.)

Weight and temperature are just two **measurable quantities**.

1 Name one instrument used for measuring temperature and one for measuring weight.
2 Can you give a unit by which weight is measured?

Of course, in everyday conversation we do not rely on instruments to give us the value of a measurable quantity. It is enough to say, for example, 'today is warmer than yesterday' or 'a pigeon flies faster than a crow'. But should we want to say 'today is 3.6°C warmer than yesterday', it would be no good relying on our senses. Our senses are good at detecting changes in quantities like light intensity, sound intensity or temperature, but instruments are required to give us values on which we can all agree. In any case, our senses can be fooled as you will discover when you carry out the first assignment in your Workbook.

There is another advantage in an instrument – its ability to measure quantities in inaccessible places, like the middle of a grain store or on the surface of Mars, both places where we would be very uncomfortable, to say the least! On Mars, the spacecrafts *Viking 1* and *2* have been taking all kinds of interesting measurements, e.g. air temperature and pressure, possibility of life in Martian soil, since they landed in 1976.

Fig. 1.1 The first photograph of the surface of the planet Mars taken by *Viking 1 Lander* only minutes after touchdown

Instruments are required for measuring quantities, such as atomic radiation, radio waves and air pressure, of which our senses are quite oblivious.

3 *Name three advantages of using instruments, rather than our senses, for measuring quantities.*
4 *What unit would you choose for measuring force?*
5 *What is the freezing point and the boiling point of pure water at sea level on Earth?*
6 *Name three instruments used in weather forecasting.*

■ Electronics and Instruments

You do not have to look far to find instruments which depend for their operation on electronics. Certainly those instruments in the *Viking* spacecrafts on Mars rely on electronic components – transistors, integrated circuits and the like – to process the information and then to send it back to Earth.

Digital clocks and watches are usually electronic. So are many of the instruments used in medicine and weather forecasting. Computing, communications and control systems today depend on electronic components. The weighing machines in most shops and laboratories are now electronic. It seems as if almost any quantity can be measured electronically. Why? Because electronic devices are cheap to produce, reliable, small, light-weight, last longer than mechanical instruments, use very little electrical power and can be easily linked to communications systems for transmission of measurements over great distances. (Remember *Viking* on Mars.) This is why you will be making and using electronic instruments in this course.

■ Instrument Parts

In this section, the essential parts required to make an instrument will be discussed. Let's begin by looking at a mechanical instrument.

A spiral spring extends when you hang a weight on the end of it (Fig. 1.2). A pointer attached to the spring will measure this extension. Hang more weight on the spring and the extension is greater. If you make up a graph of the weights and corresponding extensions, the points you plotted would fall on a near straight line for a wide range of weights (Fig. 1.3). It is then only a simple matter to use this **calibration graph** to find an unknown weight. How would you do this?

Fig. 1.2 Extension of a spring

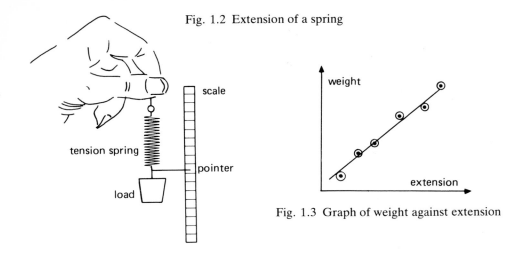

Fig. 1.3 Graph of weight against extension

An important part of this mechanical instrument for measuring weight is the pointer and scale which together display the result – an extension which corresponds to a certain weight. We shall call this the **record or display building block** of the instrument. The spring itself, that part of the instrument which responds to the quantity being measured (weight in this case), is called the **transducer building block** of the instrument.

After the transducer has done its job in responding to the quantity being measured, the response usually has to be processed in some way to make it suitable for handling by the display block. This requires a **signal processing building block**.

These three building blocks are shown linked together to form an instrumentation system as follows:

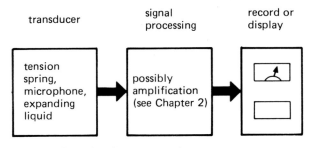

Fig. 1.4 Complete instrumentation system

7 *What transducer might you choose for an instrument for measuring sound intensity? What kind of signal processing might be required?*
8 *Write down the three building blocks in a liquid-in-glass thermometer.*

■ Current, Voltage and Resistance

These are three quantities with which you will need to become familiar if you are going to build instruments with electronic components. An instrument used for measuring any one of these quantities is shown in Fig. 1.5. It is called a **multimeter**.

Fig. 1.5 A multimeter

Instruments which have a pointer moving over a calibrated scale, as in the multimeter shown, are known as **analogue**, while those showing numbers only are known as **digital**.

9 *You have heard of digital watches and clocks but what are analogue watches?*

Digital multimeters are now replacing analogue multimeters as electronics takes over the signal processing and display functions in this instrument.

In your science lessons no doubt you will have learnt the units used for measuring current, voltage and resistance. Remember:

current is measured in **amperes**;
voltage is measured in **volts**;
resistance is measured in **ohms**.

The electronic component the **resistor** has the ability to resist the flow of electric current. An electric current can only flow through a resistor if a difference of electrical force, known as voltage difference (or **potential difference**), is applied between its ends. If this potential difference (V) is 1 volt and it produces a current (I) of 1 ampere, the resistor is said to have a resistance (R) of 1 ohm.

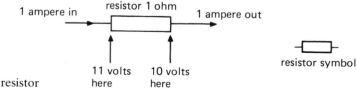

Fig. 1.6 The resistor

1 ampere in   resistor 1 ohm   1 ampere out

11 volts here   10 volts here

resistor symbol

8

But what about any voltage, current and resistance? Easy if you remember:

volts = amperes × ohms,
or $V = I \times R$.

This equation enables V, I or R to be found if you know the other two quantities. For example,

$$R = \frac{V}{I}$$

and $\quad I = \frac{V}{R}$.

The triangle shown in Fig. 1.7 is one way of remembering these equations.

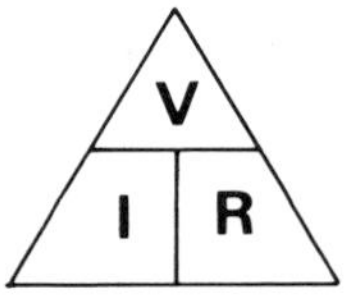

Fig. 1.7 Mnemonic symbol to help remember Ohm's law

■ Calculations

In designing and testing instruments, you will need to use the above equations. In electronic circuits we generally deal with high resistance and low currents at voltages of a few volts. For example, a voltage of 5 V across a resistor might produce a current of only two thousandths of an ampere. This can be expressed as 2 milliamps or 2 mA. The resistance of the resistor is given by:

$$R = \frac{V}{I} = \frac{5\ \text{V}}{2\ \text{mA}} = \frac{5 \times 1000}{2}$$

$$= 2500\ \text{ohms}$$
$$= 2.5\ \textbf{kilohms} = 2.5\ \text{k}\Omega$$

Now try these calculations. First you may find it helpful to carry out the measurements described in Activity 1, Assignment 2, of the Workbook.

10 *What is the voltage difference (V) required to drive a current of 1.5 mA through a 10 kΩ resistor?*

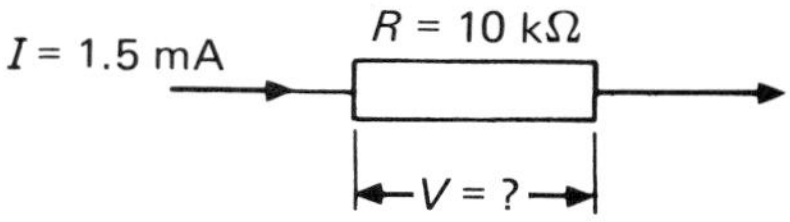

Fig. 1.8

11 *It is found that a voltage difference of 2 V sends a current of 10 μA through a resistor. What is the value of the resistor?*
(1 μA = 1/1 000 000 A or **microampere**.)

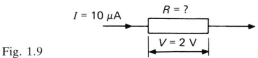

Fig. 1.9

9

■ Resistors in Series and Parallel

There are two common ways to connect resistors together, mainly for the reason that it enables you to produce a resistance of a different value. For instance, when two resistors of 5 kΩ and 2 kΩ are connected as shown in Fig. 1.10, you might not be surprised to find that the total resistance between A and B is 7 kΩ. These two resistors are connected in **series** (meaning 'one after the other'). Generally, to find the total value of resistors R_1, R_2, R_3, etc., connected in series, we use the formula:

$$R_{total} = R_1 + R_2 + R_3 + \ldots\ .$$

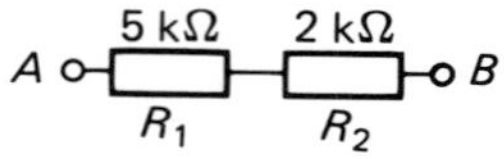

Fig. 1.10 Resistors in series

If the two resistors of 5 kΩ and 2 kΩ are connected as shown in Fig. 1.11, is the total resistance between A and B less or more than 5 kΩ? In fact, it is less than 2 kΩ and is given by the formula:

$$R_{total} = \frac{R_1 \times R_2}{R_1 + R_2}$$

$$= \frac{5 \times 2}{5 + 2}\ k\Omega = \frac{10}{7}\ k\Omega = 1.4\ k\Omega.$$

Resistors connected 'side-by-side' like this are said to be in **parallel**. The measurements described in Activity 1, Assignment 2, will help you to understand the use of the equations for series and parallel connected resistors.

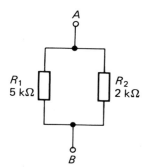

Fig. 1.11 Resistors in parallel

■ The Photocell

You now know that a transducer is important in an instrumentation system as it converts the **quantity to be measured** into a usable signal for the instrument to **process** and **display**. The **photocell** is a useful transducer as it is light sensitive. Changes of light intensity cause changes in its electrical resistance. As you will see later, this change of resistance will be used to produce a change of voltage in the instrumentation system. One type of photocell is shown in Fig. 1.12.

Fig. 1.12 A photocell

The resistance of the photocell decreases as it receives more light, the variation being shown in the graph (Fig. 1.13).

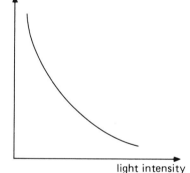

Fig. 1.13 Graph of photocell resistance against light intensity

The symbol for the photocell in our instrumentation circuits is shown in Fig. 1.14. Notice it has two terminal wires, and the arrows show it needs to receive light to make it work.

Fig. 1.14 Photocell symbol

For obvious reasons the photocell is sometimes called a **light-dependent resistor** (**LDR** for short). In the dark, the photocell's resistance is high, a million ohms (megohms) or more, but falls to less than a thousand ohms (kilohms) in daylight. Activity 1, Assignment 3, should help you become familiar with the photocell transducer.

☐ Dividing Voltage

You will often find it necessary to use resistors to divide a voltage, in order to get the correct voltage to operate a transducer or an amplifier. How can resistors divide a voltage? Look at Fig. 1.15. The two equal value resistors are connected in series between A and B with a voltage of 9 V across them.

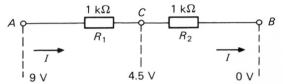

Fig. 1.15 Series resistors

Since the resistors are equal and they are connected in series, not only does the same current flow through each resistor, but the voltage across each one is the same. So the voltage at C must be 4.5 V. But what if R_1 is twice the resistance of R_2? An identical current still passes through each resistor, but resistor R_1 requires twice the voltage across it as R_2. So the voltage at C must be 3 V, since there is 6 V across R_1 and 3 V across R_2. Can you spot the general rule for working out the ratio of voltages across two resistors in series?

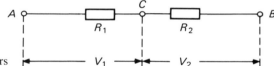

Fig. 1.16 Voltage drop across resistors

$$\frac{\text{voltage across } V_1}{\text{voltage across } V_2} = \frac{\text{resistance of } R_1}{\text{resistance of } R_2}$$

$$\frac{V_1}{V_2} = \frac{R_1}{R_2}$$

Remember that the larger resistor has the greater voltage drop across it when two resistors are connected in series. Now suppose one of the resistors is a photocell whose resistance changes as the light intensity changes (Fig. 1.17).

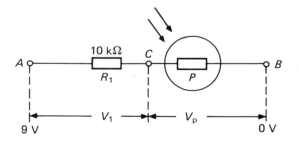

Fig. 1.17 Voltage across photocell and resistor

12

V_P is the voltage across the photocell, and V_1 the voltage across the fixed resistor R_1 of 10 kΩ in series with it.

12 *What is the voltage across the photocell when its resistance is equal to that of R_1?*

13 *What happens to the voltage across the photocell as it becomes more strongly illuminated?*

Here you will notice that the voltage at C changes as the intensity of light falling on the photocell changes. This voltage divider consisting of a transducer in series with a fixed value resistor is an important connection for an instrumentation system. The changing voltage at C operates the signal processing part of the instrument. Assignment 3 in Activity 1 will help you to understand the action of a voltage divider.

14 *A 6.8 kΩ resistor and a 3.3 kΩ resistor connected in series are to be replaced by a single resistor having the same resistance as the combination. What resistor value is required? What is the nearest value (or 'preferred' value) you would have to choose?*

15 *What is the equivalent resistance of a 330 kΩ and 100 kΩ resistor connected in parallel?*

16 *A photocell is connected in series with a resistor of 50 kΩ. The photocell is illuminated so that its resistance is 5 kΩ. If the voltage across the combination is 10 V, what is the voltage across the photocell?*

17 *What is the operating resistance of a filament lamp rated at 6 V, 60 mA?*

18 *What value of resistor reduces a 5.6 kΩ resistor to 2.2 kΩ when connected in parallel with it?*

Fig. 1.18 Artist's impression of the *Voyager* spacecraft passing the planet Saturn during 1980. This spacecraft is carrying many types of instrument to make measurements in the far reaches of the Solar System.

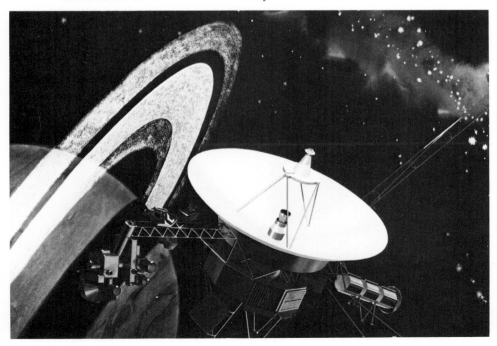

Answers to Questions

1 Thermometer; spring balance.
2 Newtons.
3 Accurate and repeatable measurements. Possibility of permanent recording of measured quantity. Ability to make measurement in remote, inaccessible or even dangerous places.
4 Newtons.
5 Freezing point 0°C.   Boiling point 100°C.
6 Thermometer – temperature; barometer – pressure; rain gauge – rainfall; hygrometer – humidity; anemometer – wind speed.
7 Microphone. Amplification.

8

Expanding liquid.	Magnification of liquid expansion through use of capillary tube.	Temperature scale.

9 Wristwatches with hands.
10 15 volts.
11 200 kΩ.
12 4.5 volts.
13 Its resistance falls so its voltage drop must also fall.
14 10.1 kΩ. 10 kΩ.
15 77 kΩ.
16 0.9 V.
17 100 Ω.
18 3.6 kΩ.

2 Transducers and Amplifiers in Black Boxes

■ What is a Black Box?

In the previous chapter, you saw how an **instrumentation system** consists of certain basic elements, which are connected together in a particular way so as to display or record the measurement being 'taken' by the system. This system is shown again in Fig. 2.1.

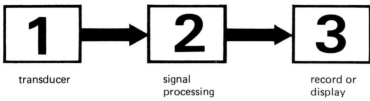

transducer   signal processing   record or display

Fig. 2.1 An instrumentation system

1 Give one example of a transducer and the quantity it responds to.
2 Name two kinds of display methods.

Notice that each element of the above instrumentation system is drawn as a box which is labelled to indicate its function. For instance, Box 2 has the function of accepting the signal from the transducer, then processing and transmitting it to the record or display box (Box 3). In order to use Box 2 in this instrumentation system, all that needs to be known are the characteristics of the signal it requires from the transducer and the properties of the signal it sends to the display. We do not need to know how Box 2 does this bit of black magic. Indeed the inner workings of Box 2 might be so complicated, and we could easily get so bogged down in trying to figure out how it works, that we might never get around to using it! Since we do not need to know how Box 2 works, we could paint it black thereby indicating that we are only interested in what it does. So a **black box** is an element of any system having information going into it which it acts upon in some way to produce the required output information.

input information   black box   output information

Fig. 2.2 Black box – input and output

3 What is the input and the output information of a photocell?

How much we include in a black box depends on how much detail we want to know about the function of the various elements in a system.

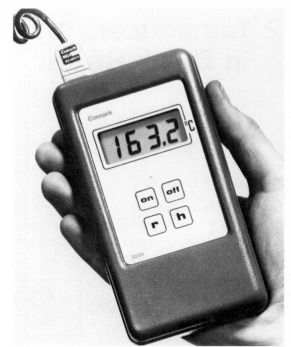

Fig. 2.3 An electronic thermometer

4 Figure 2.3 shows an electronic thermometer. What is the quantity being measured and what is the display method used?

The electronic thermometer shown in Fig. 2.3 could itself, of course, be considered to be made up of switches, amplifiers, etc., each of which could be taken as a black box. In fact, in later work you will be building instruments made up from black boxes, one of which will be an **amplifier** and one a **transducer**. Before you can make use of these elements, which are common to any instrumentation system, you will need to find out more about how they function. You have already met the photocell which is a transducer for converting changes of light intensity into changes of electrical resistance.

5 Did the resistance of the photocell rise or fall as the light intensity was reduced?

■ **Transducer Black Box – The Thermistor**

Since **temperature** is a quantity which frequently requires measuring, we need a transducer which will convert changes of temperature into a measurable electrical signal. The **thermistor** is one transducer which will do this for us, and two kinds of thermistor are shown in Fig. 2.4. On the left is a thermistor whose temperature-sensitive part is shaped like a disc, and on the right is a glass bead thermistor. Photocells and thermistors are made from semiconducting material, which is also the basis of transistors and integrated circuits.

16

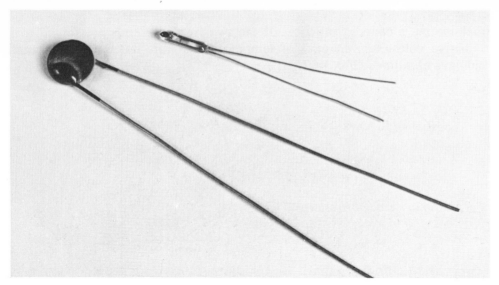

Fig. 2.4 Two types of thermistor

If you carry out Assignments 1 and 2 in Activity 2, you will find that the disc thermistor has a resistance which decreases with an increase in temperature. Furthermore, as shown in Fig. 2.5, its change of resistance with temperature is non-linear. In other words, at low temperatures a change of temperature of, say, 10°C produces a greater change of resistance than the same temperature change does at higher temperatures. There are methods of making the highly non-linear temperature-resistance characteristic of the thermistor linear, so that electronic thermometers based on them can be calibrated easily.

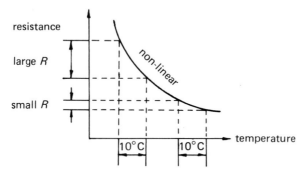

Fig. 2.5 Graph showing that a thermistor gives a non-linear
fall of resistance as the temperature increases

The thermistor is known as a **passive transducer**, since a current must be made to flow through it in order to make use of the change of resistance brought about by a change of temperature. However, a temperature transducer which provides a change of voltage with temperature, without needing an external source of electrical energy, is the **thermocouple**. This transducer is made by joining together two metal wires of different materials to

17

make what is called a junction. If the two free wire ends are joined to a sensitive voltmeter, changes of temperature at this junction cause small changes of voltage (Fig. 2.6).

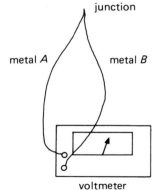

Fig. 2.6 A thermocouple transducer

Although the thermocouple transducer is much less sensitive than the thermistor transducer, it does produce a linear change of voltage with temperatures over quite large temperature ranges. As you will see in Chapter 9, a semiconductor diode can also be used as a linear temperature transducer.

6 *The thermocouple is called an* **active transducer**. *Can you say why?*
7 *Is the photocell an active or a passive transducer?*

■ Amplifier Black Box – the 741 Operational Amplifier

Since the signal voltage produced by some transducers is very small, voltage amplification is needed before the quantity being measured can be displayed. This voltage amplifier will be considered to be part of the signal processing black box and is therefore included in Box 2 of the instrumentation system (Fig. 2.7).

Fig. 2.7 Black box – signal processing

The amplifier black box is normally shown as a triangle into which the input signal (or signals) is sent, and out of which comes the amplified signal. Amplifiers also require a power supply to be connected to them but these connections to the supply are not marked in at present – see Fig. 2.8.

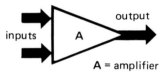

Fig. 2.8 Amplifier symbol

The particular voltage amplifier which you are going to use in building instruments really does look like a black box. It is an **integrated circuit (IC)** which has eight leads or pins used for making connections to it. The main connections to this black box are signal inputs and signal output. Figure 2.9 is a close-up of a voltage amplifier known as an **operational amplifier** (or **op amp** for short) and has the general type code of '741'. Op amps are used in computing circuits for doing mathematical operations – hence their name.

Fig. 2.9 The 741 operational amplifier
(about four times actual size)

When this op amp is drawn in our instrumentation circuits, it will look like Fig. 2.10. In all your circuits, the 741 op amp will need to be powered from a **dual power supply**. A dual power supply has three output terminals; a common (0 V), a positive supply (+V) and a negative supply (−V). The values of +V and −V are measured with respect to the common (0 V) rail. The +V connection is made to pin 7 and the −V connection to pin 4 of the 741 type IC.

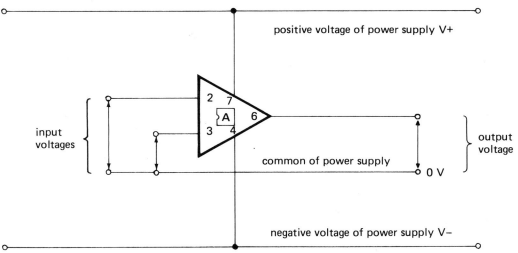

Fig. 2.10 The circuit connections for the op amp

Note that the amplifier has two input terminals, pins 2 and 3. The amplifier itself will amplify any difference of signal at these two inputs by an enormous amount – in excess of 100 000 times! Thus, in order to get output voltages of between 0 to ±5 V (compared with the ground 0 V connection) this difference of voltage between the inputs must be very small. For example, if the voltage gain is 100 000 and the output voltage is 5 V, this difference of voltage is given by:

$$\frac{5}{100\ 000} \quad \text{or} \quad \frac{50}{1\ 000\ 000}$$

This is 50 millionths of a volt. So for all practical purposes, the voltages on pins 2 and 3 can be considered to be equal.

■ Inverting and Non-inverting Inputs of the Op Amp

What determines whether the output voltage is higher (more positive) or lower (more negative) compared with the ground (0 V) connection? The answer to this depends upon whether pin 2 has a higher or lower voltage on it than pin 3 (even though the difference may be only 50 millionths of a volt). The op amp input rules are:
1 If pin 3 voltage is higher (more positive) than pin 2, the output voltage is positive.
2 If pin 2 voltage is higher (more positive) than pin 3, the output voltage is negative.
Thus a more positive voltage applied to pin 3 causes the output voltage to be positive. This input terminal is called the **non-inverting input**. A more positive voltage applied to pin 2 causes the output voltage to go negative. This input terminal is called the **inverting input**.

Assignment 3 of Activity 2 shows that a very small difference in voltage between pins 2 and 3 causes the output voltage to go sharply positive or negative.

□ Inverting and Non-Inverting Feedback Amplifiers

The voltage gain of the black box op amp (the '741') is so high that its gain needs to be 'tamed' to a more manageable size before it is useful as an instrumentation amplifier. This taming or tailoring of the op amp's voltage gain to a precisely known value is achieved by using **negative feedback**. This means that some of the output voltage (pin 6) is fed back to the inverting input (pin 2) of the amplifier by means of a feedback resistor R_f. Negative feedback is used in two circuits you will meet in designing instruments. The first type is called an **inverting feedback amplifier** (Fig. 2.11), and the second is called a **non-inverting feedback amplifier** (Fig. 2.12). Note that in these two circuits the power supply connections are not shown, but they should be made as shown in Fig. 2.10.

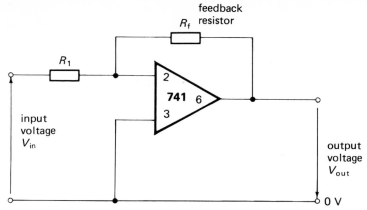

Fig. 2.11 The connections for the inverting feedback amplifier

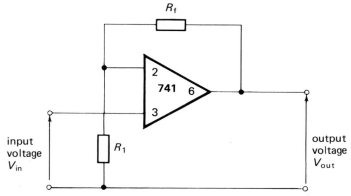

Fig. 2.12 The connections for the non-inverting feedback amplifier

There are two simple equations which define the voltage gain of these two amplifier circuits. For the inverting feedback amplifier of Fig. 2.11, the voltage gain (A) is given by the equation

$$A = \frac{\text{output voltage}}{\text{input voltage}} = \frac{V_{out}}{V_{in}} = - \frac{R_f}{R_1}$$

$$\text{or } A = - \frac{R_f}{R_1}$$

and for the non-inverting amplifier of Fig. 2.12 the voltage gain (A) is given by the equation

$$A = \frac{\text{output voltage}}{\text{input voltage}} = \frac{V_{out}}{V_{in}} = 1 + \frac{R_f}{R_1}$$

$$\text{or } A = 1 + \frac{R_f}{R_1}$$

Note that the voltage gains for these feedback amplifiers depend only on resistor values, and these can be selected to provide the exact gain required.

For example, if $R_1 = 10$ kΩ and $R_f = 500$ kΩ,

the voltage gain of the inverting feedback amplifier is given by

$$-\frac{500\text{ k}\Omega}{10\text{ k}\Omega} = -50,$$

and of the non-inverting feedback amplifier by $1 + \dfrac{500\text{ k}\Omega}{10\text{ k}\Omega} = 51.$

8 Why does the gain for the inverting feedback amplifier have a minus sign?

Assignment 4 of Activity 2 shows how negative feedback produces an amplifier with a voltage gain determined by the values of just two resistors.

☐ **The Ideal Instrumentation Amplifier**

Both of the above equations are only true if two assumptions about the amplifier hold good.
1 The voltage gain of the black box itself is very, very high (ideally infinitely large).
2 The current which flows into pin 2 or pin 3 is very, very small (ideally zero or infinitesimally small).
In practice (as stated earlier in this chapter) the gain of the 741 op amp is in excess of 100 000, which is high enough to be considered as 'infinitely large'. This high gain means that if pin 3 is connected to ground, 0 V, (as we have in Fig. 2.11 for the inverting feedback amplifier), pin 2 is also very near to 0 V. Similarly, in Fig. 2.12 for the non-inverting feedback amplifier, since the input voltage is applied to pin 3, the voltage at pin 2 follows this voltage very closely. The fact that negligible current flows into the input terminals of the op amp means that whatever current flows through R_1 in Fig. 2.11 also flows through R_f. The current which flows through R_1 is, by Ohm's Law, equal to V_{in}/R_1.

Since pin 2 can be considered to be at ground voltage (0 V), the input voltage source has, in effect, a resistor R_1 of value 10 kΩ connected across it. Thus, in order to avoid a transducer being adversely affected by current drawn from it, the value of R_1 should be high. However, since the voltage gain of the inverting amplifier is given by $(-R_f/R_1)$, R_1 should not have too high a value.

On the other hand, the non-inverting amplifier of Fig. 2.12 does not draw any current from a voltage source except for the small amount flowing into pin 3 which can be ignored. Whether a circuit uses the inverting or non-inverting connection depends on the ability of the transducer to supply a current without affecting the voltage it produces. The choice of circuits is also determined by whether a positive or negative changing voltage is required at the output. These problems are taken into account in the instrumentation circuits you will be building later.

Answers to Questions
1 Photocell; light intensity.
2 Analogue meter; digital meter.
3 Light intensity; change in electrical resistance.
4 Temperature in °C; digital display.
5 Rise.
6 Because it does not require an external power source in order to make use of its temperature change properties.
7 Passive transducer.
8 Because the output voltage is negative for a positive input voltage. This is why the arrows for the input and output voltages point in opposite directions in Fig. 2.11.

3 Digital Signal Production

■ The 555 Integrated Circuit

The 555 IC is one of a number of 'timer' integrated circuits. This group of circuits is used to provide precise time delays. Unlike the 741 op amp, this device can only give an output voltage which is either HIGH or LOW. Because the output of the 555 IC has only two possible states, it is called a **digital** device. More examples of digital circuits will be found in Chapter 5.

The 555 IC, like the 741 op amp, has eight pins (as shown in Fig. 3.1). There are two main ways of using the 555 IC: as a monostable circuit or as an astable circuit.

Fig. 3.1 Connections to the 555 integrated circuit

■ The Monostable Circuit

A **monostable circuit** is one which, once triggered, provides a HIGH output voltage for a pre-determined period of time, after which the output voltage of the circuit returns to its normal LOW state. Hence, the word 'monostable' means the circuit is stable in only one state – its state before being triggered.

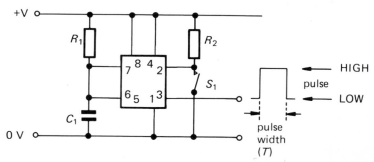

Fig. 3.2 A monostable circuit

Figure 3.2 shows the connections which must be made to the 555 in order for it to operate as a monostable circuit. When switch S_1 is closed briefly, connecting pin 2 of the integrated circuit to the 0 V power supply line, the output voltage (pin 3) rises to a value near that of the positive supply voltage. The time for which the output is HIGH is determined by the values of C_1 (a capacitor) and R_1 (a resistor). The first assignment of Activity 3 gives you an opportunity to investigate the action of a monostable circuit.

The **pulse width** is the time for which the output voltage is HIGH. For the circuit shown in Fig. 3.2, the pulse width T is given by the equation:

$T = R_1 \times C_1$ seconds, where R_1 is measured in ohms and C_1 in farads.

For example, suppose $C_1 = 100 \ \mu F$ and $R_1 = 1 \ M\Omega$. These values give:

$$T = 1 \times 10^6 \times 100 \times 10^{-6}$$
$$= 100 \text{ seconds.}$$

So, if switch S_1 is momentarily closed, the output voltage (pin 3) goes HIGH for 100 seconds and then falls to 0 V again. It remains in this state until the circuit is triggered by momentarily closing S_1 again.

■ The Astable Circuit

An **astable circuit** is a type of electronic oscillator which produces an output voltage which is switching continuously and automatically from HIGH to LOW to HIGH and so on. It is because the output voltage is not stable in either the HIGH or LOW state that this type of circuit is called 'astable'.

Figure 3.3 shows the connections which must be made to the 555 in order for it to operate as an astable circuit. The output voltage at pin 3 is a **rectangular wave**. The HIGH time is a pulse of width t_1 seconds and the LOW time is a pulse of t_2 seconds.

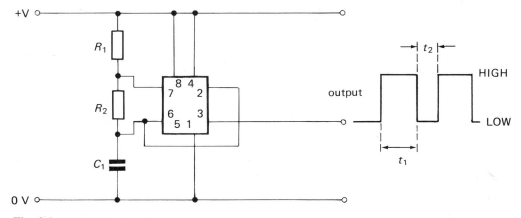

Fig. 3.3 An astable circuit

Three component values now determine these times. These are the values of R_1, R_2 and C_1.

The HIGH time t_1 is given by the equation:

$$t_1 = (R_1 + R_2) \, C_1 \text{ approximately.}$$

The LOW time t_2 is given by the equation:

$$t_2 = R_2 C_1 \text{ approximately.}$$

Both times are measured in seconds, R_1 is measured in ohms and C_1 in farads. For example, suppose $R_1 = 100 \text{ k}\Omega$, $R_2 = 50 \text{ k}\Omega$ and $C_1 = 10 \ \mu\text{F}$.

Then $t_1 = (100 \times 10^3 + 50 \times 10^3) \times 10 \times 10^{-6}$

$$= 150 \times 10^3 \times 10 \times 10^{-6}$$

$$= 1500 \times 10^{-3}$$

$$= 1.5 \text{ seconds,}$$

and $\quad t_2 = 50 \times 10^3 \times 10 \times 10^{-6}$

$$= 500 \times 10^{-3}$$

$$= 0.5 \text{ seconds.}$$

Thus, the HIGH time (when the output voltage is positive) is about 1½ seconds and the LOW time (when the output voltage is near zero) is about ½ second. Clearly, the time between the start of one HIGH pulse and the start of the next is equal to $(t_1 + t_2)$ seconds. This time is known as the **periodic time** (T) of the square wave.

$$T = t_1 + t_2$$

$$= 1.5 + 0.5 = 2 \text{ seconds.}$$

The number of HIGH pulses in one second is known as the **frequency** (f) of the square wave.

$$f = \frac{1}{T} = \frac{1}{t_1 + t_2}$$

$$= \frac{1}{2} = 0.5 \text{ Hz.}$$

Assignment 2 of Activity 3 describes how you can build and experiment with this astable circuit. The circuit will be found useful in Activity 6 when you come to build digital counting circuits.

4 Digital Signal Processors

■ Digital and Analogue Systems

Figure 4.1 shows the elements of an instrumentation system for measuring temperature. The output from the transducer (which for measuring temperature could be a thermistor) is an **analogue** or continuous signal. This means that there is a smooth change of output signal caused by changes of temperature. After amplification, the signal from the transducer operates a moving coil meter. Such an instrumentation system is known as an **analogue system**.

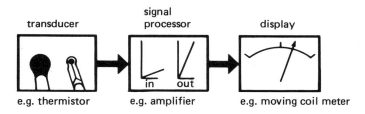

Fig. 4.1 An analogue system

Not all the quantities you will want to measure vary continuously with time. Figure 4.2 shows the elements of an instrumentation system for counting the number of pills going into a bottle.

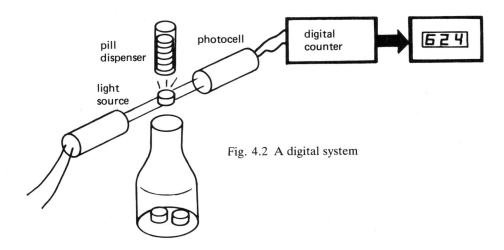

Fig. 4.2 A digital system

In this case, the number of pills (the quantity being measured) is already in a discontinuous or **digital** form. The transducer, which detects each pill entering the bottle from the pill dispenser, is a light source and photocell. The photocell is connected to a counter so that, each time a pill interrupts the light reaching the counter, the counter operates the display. Such an instrumentation system is known as a **digital system**.

1 Name two quantities which you might want to measure which are in digital form.

■ Pulses

Chapter 10 describes how you can build a circuit for measuring heart beat rate and Chapter 12 describes a circuit for measuring rotational speed. The electrical pulses obtained from a transducer which detects digital events might well have the irregular appearance shown in Fig. 4.3.

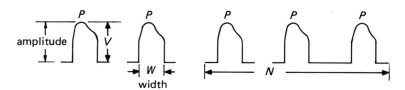

Fig. 4.3 Three characteristics of pulses

We are usually interested in just three characteristics of these pulses.
1 The 'amplitude' V of each pulse measured in volts.
2 The 'width' W or length of each pulse measured in seconds.
3 The 'number' N of these pulses which occur each second, known as the **frequency** or 'repetition rate' of the pulses.

2 What is the unit for measuring frequency?

Unfortunately, the transducers used for detecting heart beat or rotation of machinery rarely produce sets of identical pulses. Whilst their frequency might remain constant, their pulse width, pulse shape and height can well vary from one pulse to the next. This is where the Schmitt trigger circuit comes to the rescue.

■ The Schmitt Trigger Circuit

Figure 4.4 shows a Schmitt trigger circuit based on the 741 op amp. This is wired up as a voltage amplifier with a very high gain (in excess of 100 000 times), as there is no feedback resistor (see Chapter 2) between the output and inverting input, pin 2.

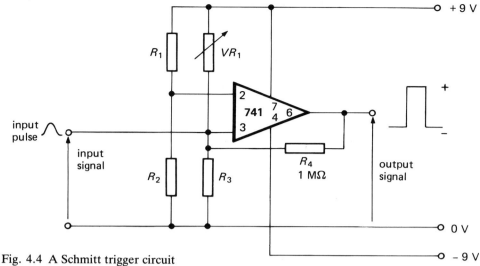

Fig. 4.4 A Schmitt trigger circuit

The variable resistor VR_1 can be adjusted to make the voltage at pin 3 of the op amp just less than the voltage on pin 2. When this happens, the voltage at pin 6, the output terminal of the op amp, is negative. Now if pin 3 receives a small amplitude positive pulse as shown in Fig. 4.4, the non-inverting input, pin 3, of the op amp is taken just above the voltage on the inverting input. This pulse therefore causes the output voltage to change sharply from a negative to a positive value. The Schmitt trigger circuit also has a resistor, R_4, connected between pin 6 and pin 3 to ensure that the output voltage 'snaps' sharply between the negative and positive voltages. This is just the sort of sharp change of voltage which is wanted for the reliable operation of a variety of electronic circuits such as the monostable circuit which you met in Chapter 3. You will be using the Schmitt trigger in Assignment 1 of Activity 4 and in Activity 10.

□ **The Integrator Circuit**

In Chapter 3 the action of a monostable circuit was described. The monostable can also be used to 'square up' irregular shaped pulses, as shown in Fig. 4.5. The irregular shaped pulses are used to trigger the monostable in the same way as S_1 was used in Fig. 3.2. Upon receipt of a positive pulse on pin 2, the circuit is triggered, remains on for its predetermined time period and then switches off. Therefore, by feeding a series of irregular pulses of a given frequency into a monostable, a series of true rectangular pulses of the same frequency, but of equal pulse width (T), are obtained. It is this type of pulse which is required to operate an **integrator circuit**.

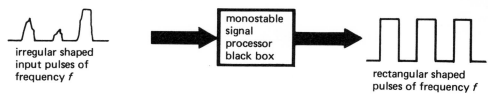

irregular shaped
input pulses of
frequency f

monostable
signal
processor
black box

rectangular shaped
pulses of frequency f

Fig. 4.5 The action of the monostable circuit

Remember that each pulse represents, say, one heart beat or one revolution of a wheel. Therefore, the higher the person's pulse rate or the faster the speed of rotation of the wheel, the higher the frequency of the pulses. Figure 4.6 shows that the pulse width from the monostable remains the same but that the pulses get closer together as the frequency increases.

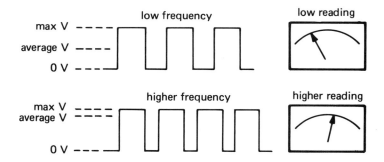

Fig. 4.6 Operating a moving coil meter

If the frequency of the pulses is doubled, the average value of voltage of these pulses is doubled. So, what is required is a device to convert these pulses (a digital signal) into an analogue reading on the meter. A device for doing this is called a **digital-to-analogue converter** or **integrator circuit**.

The simplest way to integrate the pulses is to feed them directly to a moving coil meter. Since the meter does not respond instantaneously to the rectangular pulses from the monostable circuit, it has the effect of averaging the pulses of current which flow through it. Hence, the meter produces a steady reading proportional to the frequency of the pulses from the monostable. Chapter 12 describes the design of a tachometer (for measuring rotational speed) based on this principle. (We could call the moving coil meter an **electromechanical integrator**, since it depends on the operating characteristics of the moving coil meter. Alternatively, an **electronic integrator** could be used. A circuit for doing this is shown in Fig. 4.7 and is based on a 741 op amp.

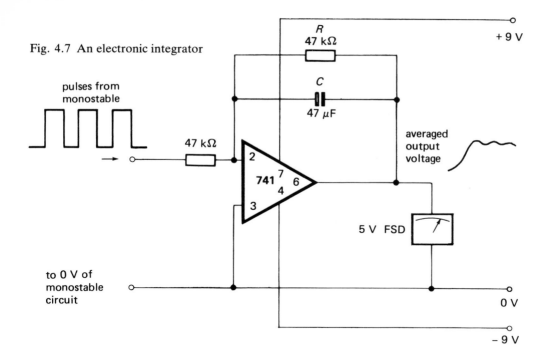

Fig. 4.7 An electronic integrator

The resistor R and capacitor C, connected in parallel between the output (pin 6) and inverting input (pin 2) of the 741 op amp, have the effect of averaging the pulses from the monostable to give a reading on the meter which is proportional to the frequency of the pulses from the monostable. Assignment 2 of Activity 4 describes how you can see this electronic integrator in action. You will find it used in the design of an instrument for measuring heart beat rate in Chapter 10.

Answers to Questions
1 Rate of rotation of a wheel in units of revolutions per minute. Heart pulse rate in beats per minute.
2 Hertz (Hz).

5 Digital Displays and Binary Numbers

■ Digital Instruments

So far, all your assignments have made use of a moving coil meter which is an **analogue display**. Figure 5.1 shows an instrument with a **digital display** or readout. Here the weight of an object is displayed as a group of digits, as opposed to a moving pointer and scale which is used in an analogue display.

Fig. 5.1 A digital display instrument

You have probably seen many kinds of instruments which have digital displays – such as watches, clocks, petrol pumps, cash registers and weighing machines. Digital displays on instruments are catching on so rapidly that they must have some advantages. What are they?

The digital read-out from a watch can be easily read at a glance. The precise time is displayed in hours and minutes. A quick glance at an analogue clockface will show an approximate value of the time. To determine the exact time, you would have to look carefully at the position of both hands on the clockface.

1 Can you think of any disadvantages of digital displays for clocks and watches?

Another advantage of a digital display is that, although most measurable quantities are in analogue form (pressure, temperature, etc), some quantities are already in digital form. The repetitive rotation of a wheel, the steady beat of the heart, the number of people at a cricket match, are examples of digital quantities which are easier to display in digital rather than in analogue form.

Fig. 5.2 Digital watch

The increasingly widespread use of digital displays in recent years has been due to the development of some very clever integrated circuits. These ICs have made the job of processing, both analogue and digital quantities, and displaying the result in digital form much simpler for the manufacturer of digital instruments. Whereas such an instrument once required dozens of transistors and ICs, nowadays a single very small **chip** of silicon can perform all the signal processing functions required to display analogue and digital quantities in digital form.

2 Name three electronic devices which you think have been the result of the miniaturisation of electronic circuits.

■ The Seven-segment Display

There are two types of seven-segment display in common use: the **light emitting diode (LED)** and the **liquid crystal display (LCD)**. Both displays are solid-state devices, the LED relying on the emission of light when a *p-n* semiconductor junction is forward biased, and the LCD relying on the transmission or absorption of certain crystals as they line up in an electric field. The main advantage of the LCD is its lower power consumption but it has the disadvantage that it cannot be seen in the dark, so watches have to be provided with an internal 'backlight' for night time viewing. You will be using only the LED seven-segment display in the assignments.

In a seven-segment LED display, seven bar-shaped LEDs are arranged in a pattern as shown in Fig. 5.3. By illuminating segments E and F, we obtain the decimal number 1. Decimal 5 is obtained by illuminating segments A, F, G, C and D, and so on. Only decimal numbers from 0 to 9 and a few special symbols (such as –) and a few alphabetical letters (such as C and F) can be displayed with seven-segment displays. The display has a decimal point either to the right or left of the digit. LED displays are available in a variety of colours: red is very common but orange, green and yellow can be obtained. Assignment 2 of Activity 5 shows how the seven-segment display works.

Fig. 5.3 The segments of a seven-segment LED display

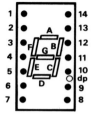

3 What alphabetic letters can be obtained with a seven-segment display?

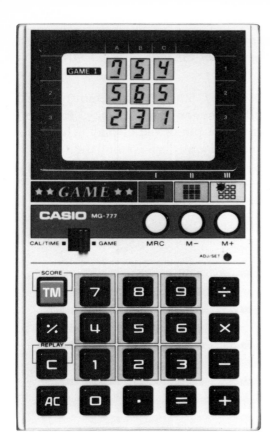

Fig. 5.4 Electronic calculator which uses an LCD

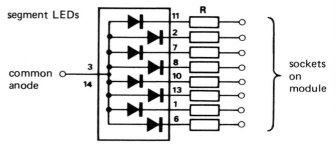

segment LEDs

common anode

sockets on module

Fig. 5.5 The light emitting diode symbols for the seven-segment display

Figure 5.5 shows the symbols of the diodes in the seven-segment display. When using an LED display (and individual LEDs), it is important to connect a resistor R in series with each diode. This resistor limits the current through, and the voltage across each diode, to the manufacturer's specifications. For example, in Fig. 5.6, the forward bias current I_f through the diode must be limited to 25 mA and the voltage V_f across it to 1.5 V. If the supply voltage $V_s = 5$ V, the value of the series resistor R is calculated as follows.

Voltage across R $= (V_s - V_f)$ volts
$= (5 - 1.5) = 3.5$ V.

Current through R $= 25$ mA (I_f).

Using Ohm's law, $V = IR$

therefore R $= \dfrac{V}{I} = \dfrac{3.5 \text{ V}}{25 \text{ mA}} = \dfrac{3.5}{2.5 \times 10^3} = 140 \ \Omega.$

The nearest preferred value of resistor you could choose would be 150 Ω.

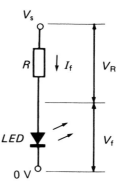

Fig. 5.6 Calculating the series resistor for an LED

35

4 For a 9 V supply, what is the value of the resistor which you must connect in series with an LED to limit the current through it to 15 mA ($V_f = 2$ V)?

Note that the anodes of all the LEDs in Fig. 5.5 are connected together, and for this reason the display is called a **common anode display**. The common anode connection is brought out to one pin of the display. There is a wide variety of pin identities for seven-segment displays but the one you will be using is a common anode display and has pins with the following functions.

Pin	Function
1	cathode A
2	cathode F
3	common anode
4	no pin
5	no pin
6	cathode decimal point
7	cathode E
8	cathode D
9	no connection
10	cathode C
11	cathode G
12	no pin
13	cathode B
14	common anode

■ The Binary Number System

A system which responds to only two possibilities is known as a **binary system**. There are many examples of binary systems – a light switch for example is either *on* or *off*. A heart beat is either *present* or *absent*. A door bell either *rings* or is *silent*. Digital electronic circuits make use of the logic of the binary system in which all the information the circuit handles is broken down into two **logic states**. These two states are logic HIGH (H) or logic LOW(L). The electrical quantity used to indicate these logic states is voltage. For example, a binary electronic system might use 0 V as logic LOW and +5 V as logic HIGH. A digital integrated circuit which responds to these high and low logic states is drawn as a black box (Fig. 5.7). It will have one or more inputs and one or more outputs.

Fig. 5.7 Digital logic black box

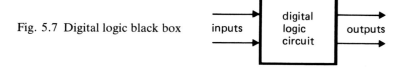

inputs   digital logic circuit   outputs

The **decimal number system** uses ten digits 0 to 9. In order to write a decimal number greater than 9, extra digits are placed in columns to the left of the first digit. Each column has a value or **weight** ten times the value of the digit immediately to its right. For example, the number 428 has three digits whose actual values are 400, 20 and 8. We can write these decimal numbers in scientific notation as powers of ten:

$400 = 4 \times 10^2$; $20 = 2 \times 10^1$; $8 = 8 \times 10^0$;

where $10^0 = 1$, $10^1 = 10$, $10^2 = 100$, $10^3 = 1000$, etc.

Thus the number $846 = 8 \times 10^2 + 4 \times 10^1 + 6 \times 10^0$.

The decimal system is said to have a **base** of ten since ten digits are used. Compare the decimal number system with the binary number system in which only two digits (called **binary digits** or **bits**) 0 and 1 are used. As with the decimal system, we write each binary number composed of 0s and 1s, giving each digit a weighting depending on its position. For example, the four-bit number $(1101)_2$ is a binary number (as the subscript 2 indicates). $(1101)_2$ is read as 'one-one-zero-one' not 'one thousand one hundred and one'.

5 Why is a binary number said to have a base of 2?

A binary number is converted into its decimal equivalent by writing each bit as a power of two in scientific notation. Thus the binary number $(1101)_2$ can be written as:

$1 \times 2^3 + 1 \times 2^2 + 0 \times 2^1 + 1 \times 2^0 = 8 + 4 + 0 + 1$

or 13 in decimal.

The table shows the binary number equivalents of some decimal numbers.

Decimal Numbers	Binary Number							Bits
	2^6	2^5	2^4	2^3	2^2	2^1	2^0	
0							0	1
1							1	1
2						1	0	2
3						1	1	2
4					1	0	0	3
5					1	0	1	3
6					1	1	0	3
7					1	1	1	3
8				1	0	0	0	4
10				1	0	1	0	4
16			1	0	0	0	0	5
23			1	0	1	1	1	5
49		1	1	0	0	0	1	6
102	1	1	0	0	1	1	0	7

6 *What is the decimal number equivalent of the highest four-bit binary number?*

7 *Write down all the binary number equivalents of the decimal numbers from 8 to 16.*

8 *What is the binary number equivalent of the decimal number 63?*

9 *What is the decimal number equivalent of $(100110)_2$?*

Answers to Questions

1 It is difficult to compare past and future time, and rapidly changing times, e.g. seconds, are not easy to follow.

2 Pocket calculator, digital wristwatch, TV games, microcomputer.

3 b, c, d, h, l, n, o, u, t; A, B, C, E, F, H, L, O, P, S, U.

4 470 Ω.

5 It has only two digits: 0 and 1.

6 15.

7 1000, 1001, 1010, 1011, 1100, 1101, 1110, 1111, 10000.

8 1111111

9 38.

6 Digital Counters

■ The Flip-flop

The **flip-flop** is a very descriptive name for a most useful digital logic device. It has two main uses. It is a device which remembers its previous logic states so it acts as a **memory** and, secondly, it is the basis of a counting system.

Figure 6.1 shows the logic symbol for the flip-flop you will be using in the assignments. It is called a **JK flip-flop** since it has two inputs, J and K, into which data can be put in order to control the logic states of its two outputs, Q and $\overline{Q}$. The flip-flop also has a clock (CLK) input which can be used to switch the outputs at the same frequency as the input clock frequency. It also has set (S) and reset (R) inputs which can be used to set the outputs to particular logic states regardless of the signals received from the clock or data inputs. Our main interest at present is in the operation of the flip-flop when its outputs are 'toggled' by the clock.

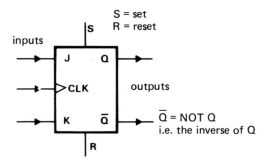

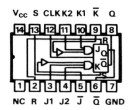

Fig. 6.1 Logic symbol for a flip-flop transistor transistor logic

Fig.6.2 The connections to the 7470 JK flip-flop (top view)

Figure 6.2 shows the connections required to the 7470 JK flip-flop. Note that this digital integrated circuit is a **TTL (transistor transistor logic)** device and needs a supply voltage of +5 V to operate it. Other kinds of IC logic devices are available and an important alternative to the TTL series of ICs are CMOS logic devices, but this kind (complementary metal oxide semiconductor) of IC will not be used in your assignments.

Each clock pulse changes the logic states of the output as you will find out in Assignment 1 of Activity 6. One output, say Q, is HIGH when the other output $\overline{Q}$ is LOW. The next clock pulse changes the logic states to

Q LOW and Q̄ HIGH. Thus the outputs are 'toggled' by the clock pulses. The outputs only change on the HIGH to LOW change of the clock pulse.

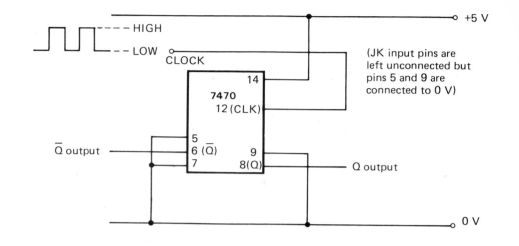

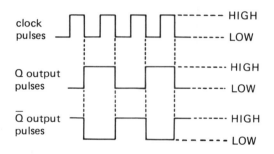

Fig. 6.3 Wiring the 7470 JK flip-flop
so that it 'toggles'

■ Flip-flop Counters

When the JK flip-flop (type 7470) is wired up as shown in Fig. 6.3, each output changes its logic state and the flip-flop is said to 'toggle'. Note that the logic state of either the Q or Q̄ output goes logic HIGH with every other clock pulse, so that the frequency of the output pulses from either output is half the frequency of the clock pulses – the flip-flop is therefore called a **divide-by-two counter**.

The **truth table** shows the logic states HIGH (H) and LOW (L) of the Q and Q̄ outputs as the flip-flop is toggled by the clock. Note that the change in the logic state of the outputs occurs on the HIGH to LOW transition of the clock pulse.

J1, J2, K1, K2 HIGH J̄ and K̄ LOW		
CLK	Q	Q̄
L	H	L
H	H	L
L	L	H
H	L	H
L	H	L

40

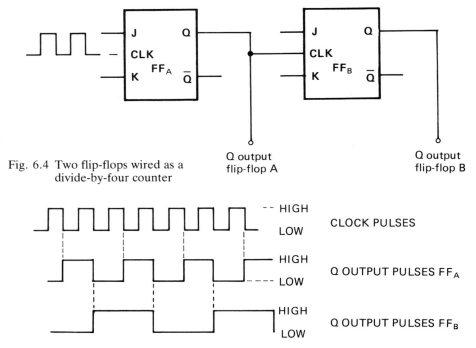

Fig. 6.4 Two flip-flops wired as a
divide-by-four counter

Q output
flip-flop A

Q output
flip-flop B

CLOCK PULSES

Q OUTPUT PULSES FF$_A$

Q OUTPUT PULSES FF$_B$

If, as shown in Fig. 6.4, the Q output of one flip-flop (FF$_A$) is connected
to the clock input of a second flip-flop (FF$_B$), the Q output of FF$_B$ changes
state once every four clock pulses. The two flip-flops make a **divide-by-
four** counter, as shown by the diagram of pulses and the truth table below.

CLK	QFF$_A$	QFF$_B$	two-bit output
L	L	H	line (a)
H	L	H	
L	H	H	line (b)
H	H	H	
L	L	L	line (c)
H	L	L	
L	H	L	line (d)
H	H	L	
RESULT 8 clock states gives →	4 QFF$_A$ states gives →	2 QFF$_B$ states, i.e. clock has been divided by 4	Note that the Q output of FF$_A$ acts as the clock input for FF$_B$.

Assignment 3 in Activity 6 describes how LEDs can be used to show the logic states of the Q outputs of FF$_A$ and FF$_B$. Since the Q outputs of these two flip-flops show two binary digits (logic HIGH or logic LOW), this divide-by-four counter is also known as a **two-bit binary counter** and has $2^2 = 4$ logic states as indicated by lines (a), (b), (c) and (d) of the previous truth table.

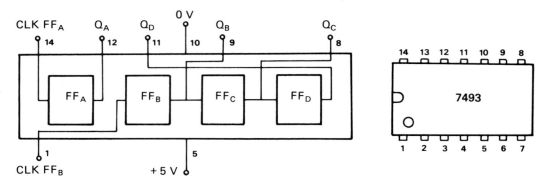

Fig. 6.5 Pin connections and internal flip-flops for the 7493 binary counter (not all connections shown)

The integrated circuit type 7493 has four internal flip-flops as shown in Fig. 6.5. The Q outputs of each flip-flop are brought out to pins 12 (Q$_A$), 9 (Q$_B$), 8 (Q$_C$) and 11 (Q$_D$). By connecting the clock to pin 14, flip-flop FF$_A$ toggles, but in order for its Q output pin 12 to operate FF$_B$, pins 12 and 1 (FF$_B$ CLK input) must be connected together externally. The truth table opposite shows that this four-bit binary counter has $2^4 = 16$ output states. Each HIGH to LOW change in voltage of the CLK pulse represents one input count. Note that the frequency of the voltage changes at the outputs are FF$_A$ (½ CLK frequency), FF$_B$ (½ × ½ = ¼ clock frequency), FF$_C$ (½ × ½ × ½ = ⅛ clock frequency) and flip-flop FF$_D$, ¹⁄₁₆th of the clock frequency.

Four-bit Output			
Input Count	Q$_D$	Q$_C$	Q$_B$	Q$_A$
0	L	L	L	L
1	L	L	L	H
2	L	L	H	L
3	L	L	H	H
4	L	H	L	L
5	L	H	L	H
6	L	H	H	L
7	L	H	H	H
8	H	L	L	L
9	H	L	L	H
10	H	L	H	L
11	H	L	H	H
12	H	H	L	L
13	H	H	L	H
14	H	H	H	L
15	H	H	H	H

■ The BCD Counter

The 7493 integrated circuit produces a four-bit binary coded output count from 0 to 15 $(1111)_2$ before automatically resetting to zero. However, if we are to operate a conversion circuit for changing binary counts to decimal digits, the maximum four-bit output pulse must be $(1001)_2$, equivalent to decimal 9. The next count should reset to zero.

A counter which produces the ten decimal numbers 0 to 9 in four-bit binary form, as shown opposite, is known as a **binary-coded decimal (BCD) counter**. Although it is possible to make the 7493 operate as a BCD counter, it is not necessary to do so since the 7490 BCD counter is made for the job. Assignment 4 in Activity 6 will give you an opportunity to show the action of this BCD counter.

Input Count	Four-bit Output			
	Q_D	Q_C	Q_B	Q_A
0	L	L	L	L
1	L	L	L	H
2	L	L	H	L
3	L	L	H	H
4	L	H	L	L
5	L	H	L	H
6	L	H	H	L
7	L	H	H	H
8	H	L	L	L
9	H	L	L	H

■ BCD to Seven-segment Display Decoder/Driver

Since the output from most digital systems is in binary form, some kind of signal processing is required to convert this binary signal into the more readily understood decimal form. However, since this decoder is also required to provide sufficient current to light the segment LEDs of a seven-segment display, the decoder will also contain a 'driver' which provides sufficient current to drive the LED segments. Thus the full name of this decoder is a **BCD to seven-segment display decoder/driver**.

Each segment may require 10 mA current so, including the decimal point, the maximum current the decoder must supply is 8×10 mA = 80 mA. This current, of course, comes from the supply to the decoder.

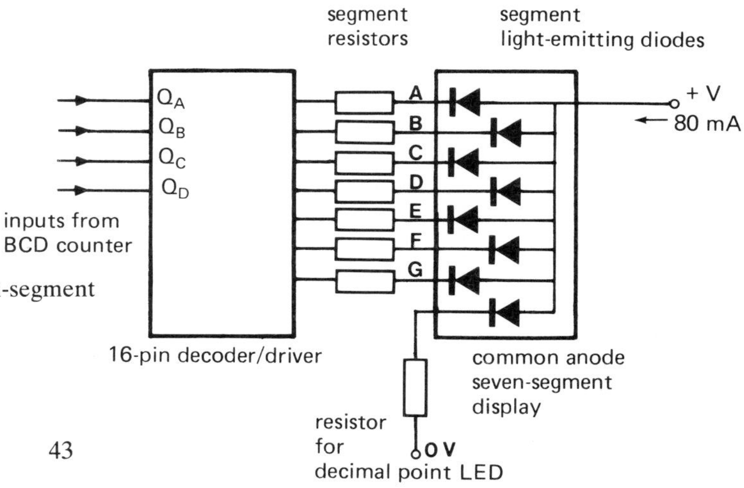

Fig. 6.6 Wiring connection of the seven-segment display to the decoder/driver

43

Decimal Number	Logic States of Decoder Inputs				Logic States of Decoder Outputs to Segment Cathodes						
	Q_A	Q_B	Q_C	Q_D	A	B	C	D	E	F	G
0	L	L	L	L	L	L	L	L	L	L	H
1	L	L	L	H	H	H	H	H	L	L	H
2	L	L	H	L	L	L	H	L	L	H	L
3	L	L	H	H	L	L	L	L	H	H	L
4	L	H	L	L	H	L	L	H	H	L	L
5	L	H	L	H	L	H	L	L	H	L	L
6	L	H	H	L	H	H	L	L	L	L	L
7	L	H	H	H	L	L	L	H	H	H	H
8	H	L	L	L	L	L	L	L	L	L	L
9	H	L	L	H	L	L	L	H	H	L	L

Figure 6.6 shows the black box decoder/driver connected to a common anode seven-segment display. The table shows how the inputs to the decoder/driver (from the preceding BCD counter) are decoded to drive the appropriate segments of the display which shows the corresponding decimal number equivalent. For example, if the four-bit number is $(0110)_2$ corresponding to decimal 6, segments C, D, E, F and G must light up as shown in Fig. 6.7. With a common anode seven-segment display, the C, D, E, F and G outputs of the decoder must go LOW (outputs A and B remain HIGH).

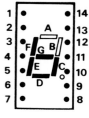

Fig. 6.7 Seven-segment display (decimal number 6)

Assignment 4 in Activity 6 shows how to a build a counting circuit using the TTL BCD seven-segment display decoder/driver type 7447.

7 Light Intensity Meter

■ Light Intensity

In this chapter, you will see how to connect together electronic devices so that **light intensity** can be measured. Apart from ensuring that the environment in which we live and work is adequately lit, there are many technical developments which demand accurate light intensity measurement: taking a photograph and constructing electronic circuits, for example. The undeveloped film in the camera must receive just the right amount of light in order for it to be exposed correctly. To take a good picture, a **light meter** (Fig. 7.1) is required.

Fig. 7.1 A photographic light meter

You can no doubt think of other technical developments which require an accurate knowledge of light intensity.

1 Name a unit in which light intensity is measured.

■ The Unit of Light Intensity

Over the years, there have been many units used to measure light intensity. The SI recommended unit is the **lux**. The lux concerns the amount of light energy falling on a surface in one second, that is **illumination**. The unit is related to the light emitted from a standard light source called the **candela** (not so very different from the light emitted from a wax candle – the earlier standard light source). These days, the candela is a special kind of electric lamp kept at places like the National Physical Laboratory for the purpose of calibrating light meters.

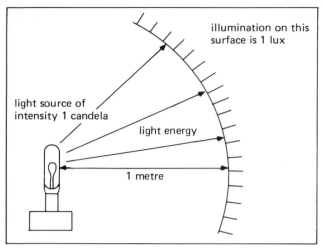

Fig. 7.2 The meaning of a lux, the unit of illumination

An illumination of one lux is produced one metre away from a light source of one candela, as Fig. 7.2 shows. A few examples will give you an idea of the size of the lux.

On a bright summer's day, the illumination of the ground is about 100 000 lux, while a bright moonlit night provides about 0.1 lux. If test match cricket at Lords has to stop due to bad light, the illumination is below about 50 lux. In a well lit room on a bright day, illumination is about 200 lux, while reading requires a minimum of 30 lux and, for fine work, at least 500 lux.

Note that the eye has the ability to see over the range 100 000 lux to 0.1 lux without discomfort – an enormous range of levels of illumination of a million to one! An instrument of the kind shown in Fig. 7.3 can measure a wide range of levels of illumination and might be used for determining whether the lighting in offices or factories meets the levels required by law.

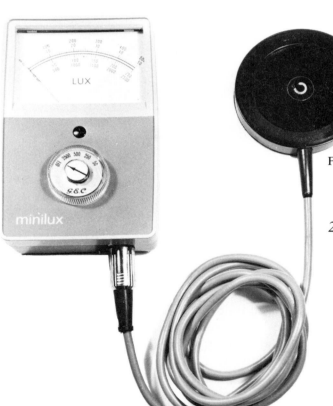

Fig. 7.3 A commercial light meter

2 How many scales has the lux meter and do the calibrations appear to be linear?

■ A Light Intensity Transducer

In Chapter 2, a device which responds to change in light intensity was examined. This device is called a photocell. It was shown that the electrical resistance of the photocell decreases as the light intensity increases (see Fig. 7.4).

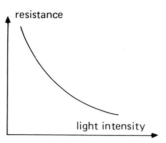

Fig. 7.4 The change of resistance of the photocell with light intensity

Although the change of resistance is large for a small change of light intensity, the resistance is not proportional to light intensity. There are ways of straightening out the curve using a special circuit so that a moving coil meter can be used to display the light intensity, but the circuit is not easy to set up. Fortunately, another type of transducer comes to the rescue. It is known as a **photodiode**, and one type is shown in Fig. 7.5.

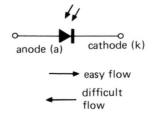

Fig. 7.5 A photodiode

The photodiode is so-called for two reasons. Firstly, it has two leads (*di*ode) and current flows easily through it one way and has trouble doing so the other way. Secondly, current flowing through it the difficult way changes with light intensity. The symbol for the diode is shown in Fig. 7.6 and the easy (forward biased) and difficult (reverse biased) current directions. Note the names for the two leads, anode and cathode.

Fig. 7.6 The behaviour of a photodiode

anode (a)   cathode (k)

→ easy flow

← difficult flow

47

What is very important about the small current which flows through the diode, when it is reverse biased, is that it is proportional to light intensity if the voltage is kept constant. This very important characteristic is shown in Fig. 7.7.

Fig. 7.7 The reverse bias characteristic of the photodiode

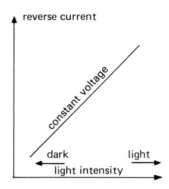

The reverse bias current is very small and varies with light level, from about 1 nanoamp when dark (nA or 10^{-9}A) to about 1 milliamp (mA or 10^{-3}A) in full daylight. How can this linear change of reverse bias current with light intensity be used?

☐ **A Special Amplifier for the Photodiode**

Figure 7.8 shows a simple amplifier circuit based on the 741 op amp which produces an output voltage given by the equation:

$$V_{out} = I \times R \text{ where } I \text{ is the reverse current through the diode and } R \text{ is the value of the feedback resistor.}$$

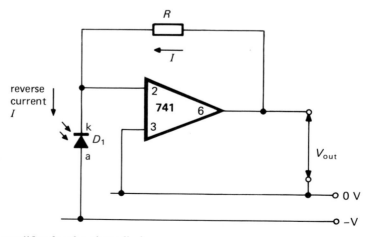

Fig. 7.8 An amplifier for the photodiode

48

This circuit is quite simple in its operation and relies upon the very high gain of the op amp. In Chapter 2, it was shown that the differential voltage between the two inputs was virtually zero and that for all practical purposes, pins 2 and 3 can be considered to be at the same potential. In this circuit, because pin 3 is connected to 0 V then pin 2 is at 0 V also. As the anode of D_1 is connected to the negative supply rail and its cathode to pin 2 (0 volts), the diode is reverse biased. The reverse voltage is constant and equal to the negative supply voltage. By referring to Fig. 7.7, it can be seen that if the light intensity falling on the diode is reversed, then the current flowing through it will increase. This reverse current must come from somewhere and, due to the design of the op amp, it cannot come from pin 2, so it must be supplied through R (the feedback resistor) from the output.

The pin 2 end of R must also be at 0 V for the same reasons as described above, so the voltage drop across R will be the product of I (the diode reverse current) and R. This means that the output voltage is directly proportional to the reverse current through the diode and is given by the equation:

$$V_{out} = I \times R.$$

Assignment 2 in Activity 7 describes how to construct this very simple linear light meter.

Answers to Questions
1 Lux.
2 4; yes.

8 Noise Intensity Meter

■ Noise

This chapter is going to look at one aspect of the measurement of noise intensity. The Workbook assignments show how to build a simple instrument which can be used to make a rough measurement of noise intensity.

It can be thought that noise is an environmental problem brought about by the widespread growth of communications, industrialisation, transportation and population of the twentieth century. As a matter of fact, for centuries English law has recognised the individual's right to 'quiet enjoyment'.

Noise is a kind of pollution of the air and, like chemical pollution in the environment, it can be very harmful, causing deafness and serious illness when it is excessive and prolonged. This is the reason why the control of noise is the responsibility of the local health inspector.

Fig. 8.1 Noisy surroundings

One of the main problems of measuring noise is that opinions differ as to what is noise and what is pleasant to listen to. One person's noise is another person's music! Of course, an instrument to measure noise intensity cannot respond to these human subjective and psychological differences, although it can be designed to mimic the way the human ear responds to the differing frequencies and intensities of sounds.

1 What is the difference between noise and sound?
2 What is the difference between a psychological effect and physiological effect on our body?

☐ The Decibel

Sound waves in the air around us are the result of very small and rapid changes of air pressure. Like any pressure, sound pressure is measured in units of newtons per square metre (**N/m²**). The human ear is very sensitive since the smallest pressure change it can detect is about 0.000 02 N/m², the so-called **threshold of hearing**, which is about one ten thousand millionth of normal air pressure (10^5 N/m²). Sounds below this pressure are 'silent' to us. As the pressure changes increase in magnitude, the sounds we hear get louder but they have to increase to about 10 N/m² before the sounds become painful to listen to. So painful sounds, at the so-called **threshold of pain**, are caused by air pressure changes over a million times greater than those which are just audible at the 'threshold of hearing'. Surprisingly, our ears can cope with this enormous range of pressure changes and they do it in an interesting way:

> equal increases in the perceived sound level are caused by the sound pressure being multiplied by a constant factor.

This response is **logarithmic** and gives rise to the unit for measuring sound intensity, which is called a **decibel**. On the decibel scale of sound intensities, the threshold of hearing at 0.000 02 N/m² is given a value of 0 dB. Every tenfold increase in sound pressure is given a constant value of 20 dB increase. This scale is shown in the table below. Thus, after six steps, each ten times the sound pressure just before it, we reach 120 dB, the threshold of pain.

Sound Pressure (N/m²)		Sound Pressure Level (decibels)
2×10	Threshold of pain	120 dB
2×10^0		100 dB
2×10^{-1}		80 dB
2×10^{-2}		60 dB
2×10^{-3}		40 dB
2×10^{-4}		20 dB
2×10^{-5}	Threshold of hearing	0 dB

3 If the sound pressure doubles, the sound level on this logarithmic scale increases by 3 dB. How many doublings of sound pressure take place in the range 65 dB to 92 dB?

4 Two sources of sound, each of level 70 dB, are sounded at the same time. What is their combined level in dB?

An instrument designed to measure noise must behave in this logarithmic way if it is to respond as the ear does. Unfortunately, there is a complicating characteristic of the ear which has to be taken into account – its **frequency response**.

The sound pressure produced by some typical sounds and their equivalent sound pressure levels in decibels are shown in the table below.

Sound Pressure (N/m²)	Sound Pressure Level (dB)	Typical Sounds
2×10^{-5}	0 (threshold of hearing)	Leaves rustling.
2×10^{-4}	20	Quiet country lane. Rustle of paper.
2×10^{-3}	40	Quiet office. Inside average home.
2×10^{-2}	60	Normal conversation at 1 metre. Busy street.
2×10^{-1}	80 (danger level)	Inside small car. Underground train.
2	100	Food blender at 0.5 metres. Pop group at 2 metres.
2×10	120 (threshold of pain)	Jet aircraft at 200 metres. Jet engine at 30 metres.
2×10^2	140	
2×10^3	160	Skin can be burned by sound at speech frequencies.
2×10^4	180	Can kill.
2×10^5	200	Noise weapon.

■ Frequency Response of the Ear

The normal human ear responds to sound in the frequency range 20 Hz to 16 kHz, but the response varies from individual to individual and with age. As we get older, our ears become progressively less sensitive to the higher frequencies. However, even the normal ear is less sensitive to a sound of frequency about 3 kHz. Commercial noise meters, like the one shown in Fig. 8.2, take this into account so that their frequency response is similar to that of the ear.

Fig. 8.2 A commercial noise meter

5 *The sound pressure inside the cab of a lorry might very well be the same as that produced by a fire alarm siren. Why does the alarm sound much louder?*

A noise meter is designed to respond like the human ear by incorporating an amplifier in its electronic circuits, which gives less voltage gain at low and high frequencies. The amplifier is said to be **weighted** in favour of frequencies in the range 1 kHz to 4 kHz, giving a so-called **dBA** weighted scale on a sound intensity meter. For a 100 Hz frequency tone, the effect results in a noise meter giving a dBA reading 19 dB lower than the actual sound pressure.

53

■ An Electronic System for a Sound Meter

The first requirement is a transducer which converts variations of air pressure due to sound into electrical signals. It should be no surprise to you to find that this is a **microphone**.

The signals from the microphone are fed into an electronic amplifier which produces a weighted amplification of signals in the 1 kHz to 4 kHz range of frequencies, just as the ear does. The resulting scale is calibrated in dBA.

Before a meter is operated, these weighted audio frequency electrical signals need processing further. They must be rectified, in order to operate a dc meter, and they may also need to be attenuated, so that the sound meter can have a number of dBA scales, e.g. 45 to 60 dB, 55 to 70 dB, etc. The black box system for the sound meter would therefore be as shown in Fig. 8.3.

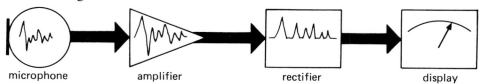

microphone   amplifier   rectifier   display

Fig. 8.3 The electronic system for a noise meter

The design of a rugged, reliable and accurate noise meter is very complex. However, it is quite easy to make an instrument which will give an approximate indication of sound pressure level, provided you have an accurate noise meter to calibrate it against. The Workbook assignments will give you some experience of building the circuit involved.

■ A Simple Noise Meter Circuit

The circuit shown in Fig. 8.4 is more of a noise 'level indicator' than a meter, since it is designed to turn on a light when the noise level exceeds a certain preselected value.

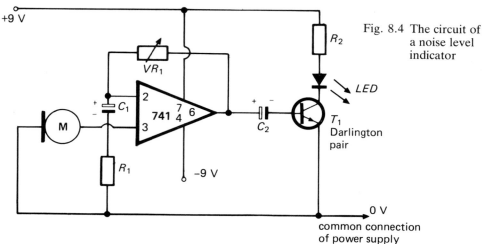

Fig. 8.4 The circuit of a noise level indicator

common connection of power supply

54

In Fig. 8.4, the amplifier (A) is a 741 op amp and is wired up as a non-inverting audio frequency amplifier. The microphone (M) picks up the sound waves and converts them into electrical signals which are passed on the non-inverting input terminal 3 of the amplifier. Components VR_1, C_1 and R_1 enable the amplifier to operate as an ac amplifier, the voltage gain of which is determined by the ratio of VR_1 to R_1.

The amplified audio frequency signal from the amplifier is fed into the electronic switch based on the *n-p-n* transistor T_1. This transistor is able to switch on and pass enough current to switch on the light emitting diode if the signal from the amplifier passing through the capacitor is greater than 1.2 V. The transistors only switch on if the base-to-emitter voltage of the transistors exceeds 1.2 V, so that these transistors act as a rectifier. The variable resistor VR_1 is adjusted so that, for a particular sound intensity, the LED just lights. Thus VR_1 could be calibrated in sound level units of dBA by comparison with an already calibrated sound level meter. Note that transistor T_1 should be a Darlington pair type which has two transistors connected together.

Assignment 3 of Activity 8 gives you an opportunity to study this simple noise meter circuit.

Answers to Questions

1 Noise is unwanted sound.

2 Noise can cause physical damage to the hearing mechanism in the inner ear which changes sounds into nerve impulses. This is a physiological change. Noise can also cause tiredness and make us annoyed with the people generating the sound – a psychological effect.

3 $\dfrac{92 - 65}{3}$ = 9 doublings of sound pressure.

Thus the sound pressure at 92 dB is $2 \times 2 \times 2 \times 2 \times 2 \times 2 \times 2 \times 2 \times 2$ = 512 times the sound pressure at 65 dB.

4 73 dB.

5 The ear is more sensitive to the high frequencies of the siren and less sensitive to the low frequencies in the cab of the lorry.

9 Thermometer

■ Heat and Temperature

Before designing a thermometer, let's try and clear the confusion which arises from the use of the words 'heat' and 'temperature'. A thermometer measures temperature not heat. For example, if a thermometer is used to measure the temperature of a match flame, the thermometer will record about 800°C (see Fig. 9.1). Now light a bonfire with the match and use the same thermometer to measure the temperature of the bonfire. Much the same reading will be obtained, about 800°C. The bonfire is producing much more heat than the lighted match, but the thermometer only responds to the intensity of the heat, not how much of it there is.

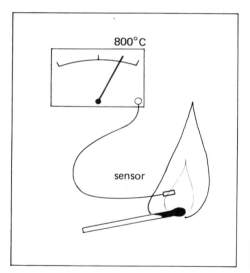

Fig. 9.1 The difference between heat and temperature – lighted match same temperature as bonfire

Unfortunately, all thermometers need to take some heat energy from the object whose temperature is being measured, but the less heat required the better. There is no point in having a thermometer which needs so much heat to work it that it cools the object whose temperature it is supposed to be measuring. One of the advantages of electronic thermometers is that the sensors (transducers) need very little heat to work them.

56

One further point, concerning thermometers which rely on actual contact with the object whose temperature is being measured, is that once the thermometer has reached a steady reading, its sensor is at the same temperature as the temperature of the object. It is said that the sensor must be in **thermal equilibrium** with the object of its measurement.

1 Can you name two units for measuring heat?

■ Units of Temperature

Temperature is measured in degrees Celsius (C), although some technologists prefer to measure it in degrees Kelvin (K).

2 What are the normal boiling and freezing points of water on the Celsius scale?
3 Do you know the theoretically predicted lowest temperature attainable on the Celsius scale? Is there a theoretically predicted highest possible temperature?

■ Choosing a Transducer

In Chapter 2 it was found that a thermistor is a device which can respond to changes in temperature. It was shown that the electrical resistance of a thermistor decreases as the temperature increases, as shown in Fig. 9.2.

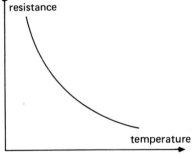

Fig. 9.2 The change of resistance of the thermistor with temperature

Although the change of resistance of the thermistor is large for a small change of temperature, the resistance is not directly proportional to the temperature. There are ways of straightening out this curve, just as for a photocell, to enable a moving coil meter to be used to display temperature, but the circuit is not easy to set up. Fortunately, another type of transducer can be used. This device is an ordinary diode used in rectifying circuits. The appearance of such a diode and the forward bias characteristic of it is shown in Fig. 9.3

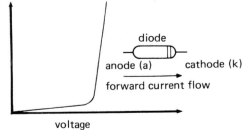

Fig. 9.3 The forward bias characteristic of the diode

There is a very useful property of the forward bias current of this diode. Provided the current through the diode from anode to cathode is kept constant, the voltage across the diode is proportional to temperature, as shown in Fig. 9.4. Note the voltage falls as temperature increases.

Fig. 9.4 The linear relationship between voltage and temperature

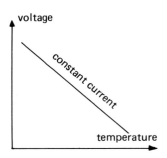

All that is necessary is a circuit which provides a constant forward current through the diode, and then measures the voltage across the diode as the temperature changes.

■ A Constant Current Generator

The circuit shown in Fig. 9.5 will generate the necessary constant current through the diode. This circuit is very similar to that described in Chapter 7 for light measurement. As pin 3 is connected to 0 V, pin 2 is also at 0 V, and so R has a constant voltage across it. This means that a constant current will flow through R, given by:

$$I = \frac{V}{R}$$

Fig. 9.5 A constant current generator

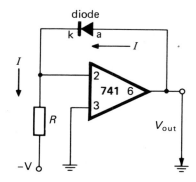

This constant current also flows through the diode since it is in series with R, and negligible current flows into the amplifier.

4 What is this current if $V = 10$ volts and $R = 100$ kΩ?

□ An Inverting Amplifier

The decrease in voltage across the diode as its temperature increases is very small – about 2 mV for every degree Celsius. This voltage can be amplified by the amplifier part of the circuit shown in Fig. 9.6.

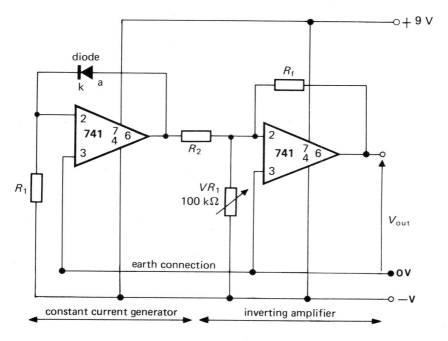

Fig. 9.6 Inverting amplifier and diode temperature transducer

The voltage gain of the amplifier is given by the ratio R_f/R_2 and can easily be preset to give different temperature ranges on the meter. Thus if R_f = 1 MΩ and R_2 = 10 kΩ, the voltage gain is 100. This gain is sufficient to amplify the small output voltage from the diode transducer. For example, suppose the voltmeter has an FSD of 1 V. The input voltage change for a gain of 100 is therefore 1 V/100 or 10 mV. Since the preceding circuit produces an output voltage of 2 mV per °C, the temperature range which can be recorded is 5°C.

5 *What would the gain of the inverting amplifier need to be if a range of 50°C had to be displayed on the 1 volt FSD meter? What value would R_2 need to have if R_f = 1 MΩ?*

Some means of setting the thermometer to zero is necessary, and this is achieved by VR_1 (Fig. 9.6). If, for example, the meter was to be used to indicate a temperature range from 0°C to 20°C, the 100 kΩ variable resistor can be used to adjust the voltage on pin 2 to set the output voltage to zero when the diode is at a temperature of 0°C.

Assignment 2 in Activity 9 shows how to set up this circuit for a linear thermometer. Finally, Fig. 9.7 is a black box diagram of this linear thermometer showing what happens to the signals the transducer generates.

Fig. 9.7 The electronic system used for the thermometer

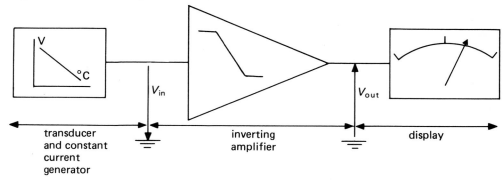

Answers to Questions
1 Calorie; joule.
2 Boiling 100°C; freezing 0°C.
3 −273°C; no.
4 $I = \dfrac{10 \text{ V}}{100 \text{ k}\Omega} = \dfrac{10}{10^5} = 10^{-4}\text{A or } 0.1 \text{ mA}.$
5 1000; 1 kΩ.

10 Pulse Rate Meter

■ Why Measure Heart Beats?

In this chapter, you are going to see how to design a circuit to record automatically the rate at which your heart beats. Once again this means connecting together a number of electronic circuit elements (black boxes) in order to display your pulse rate in beats per minute on a moving coil meter.

If you are an athletic type, a pulse rate meter will enable you to find out if you are really fit, since a fit person's heart rate returns to normal after exercise more rapidly than an unfit person's. Or perhaps you are interested in trying to control the rate at which your heart beats in order to relax more fully? By concentrating on the meter reading and willing it to change, you would be using a technique known as **biofeedback** – much in the news these days. Other bodily functions (even brain waves!) can be controlled in this way. Biofeedback means consciously controlling biological functions which are normally involuntary (not consciously controlled) by using your senses as the feedback path.

1 Take your pulse. (Your teacher will explain how to do this.) What do you think is your normal pulse rate and what units do you measure it in?
2 What is an electrocardiograph? What is an electroencephalograph?

■ What Kind of Transducer?

Any kind of muscle activity, including the regular contraction of the heart, is triggered by electrical signals from the brain. The shape of the electrical patterns associated with each heart beat is recorded because it provides information about the state of health of the heart; this is the purpose of the **electrocardiograph** and, as Fig. 10.1 shows, interest in the cardiac electrical signals is not new. However, even though the technique has improved over the years with advances in electronics, picking up the very low amplitude signals at the surface of the body is still very difficult.

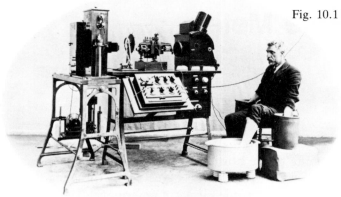

Fig. 10.1 A good many years ago the recording of electrical signals from the heart appeared to be a risky business

Instead of trying to detect the low amplitude electrical signals from the heart, we could try and detect a secondary effect of the heart beat. The method chosen here makes use of a **photocell**. This transducer detects the very small change of light intensity with each heart beat as light passes through a fleshy part of the body – your earlobe or finger tip, for example.

3 What happens to the resistance of a photocell when less light reaches it?

■ Picking up a Signal

The change in resistance of the photocell for each heart beat is very small (about 100 ohms) since the transmission of light through the finger is not decreased very much with each pulse of blood. The amplifier black box described in Chapter 2 can readily amplify small voltage changes. This means that the small change of resistance must be converted into a change of voltage to operate this type of amplifier. One way of doing this is with the circuit shown in Fig. 10.2, which uses a 741 integrated circuit black box amplifier.

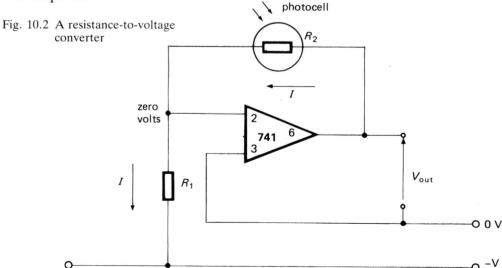

Fig. 10.2 A resistance-to-voltage converter

This circuit works in a similar manner to the one described in Chapter 9 for sensing temperature. The resistor R_1 is connected between the negative supply rail $(-V)$ and pin 2 (zero volts), thus a current flows through it. The value of I can be found from the equation:

$$I = \frac{0-(-V)}{R_1}$$

$$= \frac{V}{R_1}$$

As has been stated previously, a negligible current flows into pin 2 of the 741 amplifier, thus the current I must flow through R_2 (the resistance of the photocell). The current flowing in R_2 is given by:

$$I = \frac{V_{out} - 0}{R_2}$$

$$= \frac{V_{out}}{R_2}$$

Because the current flowing through R_1 and R_2 is the same, the two equations above must be equal.

So $$\frac{V}{R_1} = \frac{V_{out}}{R_2}$$

therefore $$V_{out} = \frac{R_2 \times V}{R_1}$$

If $V = 10$ V and $R_1 = 100$ kΩ

then $$V_{out} = \frac{R_2 \times 10}{100 \times 10^3}$$

$$= \frac{R_2}{10\ 000}$$

Because R_2 changes by about 100 ohms each time blood is pumped through the finger, V_{out} changes by:

$$\frac{100}{10\ 000} = \frac{1}{100} \text{ volts or 10 mV.}$$

This is a very small change of voltage, so an amplifier is required to bring this voltage up to a more useful level.

■ An Inverting Amplifier

The circuit in Fig. 10.3 shows a black box voltage amplifier similar to that described in Chapter 2, where it was shown that the voltage gain is given by:

$$\frac{V_{out}}{V_{in}} = -\frac{R_f}{R_1}$$

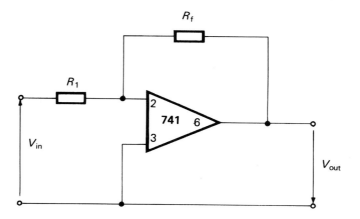

Fig. 10.3 An inverting amplifier

Note the minus sign indicates that the output is inverted compared with the input. If this amplifier is connected to the resistance-to-voltage conversion circuit shown in Fig. 10.2, the input voltage V_{in} will be 10 mV.

With R_f = 1 MΩ and R_1 = 10 kΩ,

$$V_{out} = -\frac{V_{in} \times R_f}{R_1}$$

$$= -\frac{10 \times 10^{-3} \times 1 \times 10^6}{10 \times 10^3}$$

$$= -\frac{10^4}{10^4}$$

$$= -1 \text{ volt.}$$

This means that with an input voltage of 10 mV, the output voltage will be 1 volt (inverted). So the amplifier has a gain of −100.

□ Shaping the Signal

Before the signal from the inverting amplifier can operate a moving coil meter calibrated in beats per minute, the signal from the inverting amplifier must be shaped. Two pulse-shaping circuits are required, followed by an electronic integrator. These circuits are:
 1 Schmitt trigger (Chapter 4);
 2 Monostable (Chapter 3);
 3 Integrator (Chapter 4).

□ Schmitt Trigger

The Schmitt trigger circuit in Chapter 4 is based on a 741 op amp connected so that a small charge of voltage at its non-inverting input produces a much larger charge in output voltage as shown in Fig. 10.4.

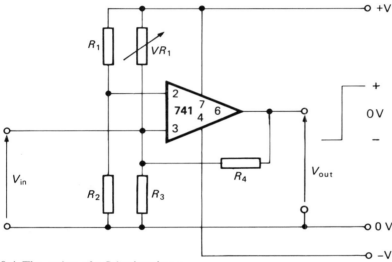

Fig. 10.4 The action of a Schmitt trigger

One input of the op amp, pin 2 in this case, is maintained at a constant voltage by the voltage divider R_1 and R_2. If the voltage, V_{in} on pin 3, the non-inverting input of the op amp, is below the pin 2 voltage, the output voltage, V_{out}, is negative. But if the input voltage is just above that on pin 2, the output voltage rises sharply to a positive value. Due to the action of resistor R_4, the voltage on pin 2 must fall slightly below the voltage which first made V_{out} positive in order to make V_{out} negative once again. Thus the Schmitt trigger acts as a 'snap action' electronic switch. Resistor VR_1 enables you to choose the voltage level at which the circuit switches over. That is, it acts as a sensitivity control. Assignment 3 in Activity 10 shows a practical application of the Schmitt trigger circuit.

□ Monostable

The monostable circuit in Chapter 3 is based on a 555 timer integrated circuit. As Fig. 10.5 shows, the monostable is able to produce voltage pulses
of a fixed duration at the same frequency as the input pulses. It does not
matter if these input pulses vary in shape or height.

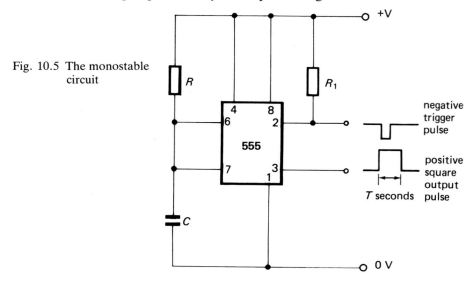

Fig. 10.5 The monostable circuit

□ Integrator

This circuit was described in Chapter 4. It provides a steady output voltage
proportional to the average of the input pulses. Since the area of each in
put pulse coming from the monostable remains constant, the steady output
voltage from the integrator is proportional to the frequency of the input
pulses. This is precisely what is required to drive the display of the pulse
rate meter. Figure 10.6 shows the action of an electronic integrator based
on the 741 op amp.

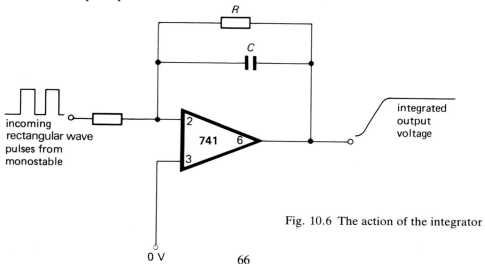

Fig. 10.6 The action of the integrator

■ Block Diagram of Pulse Rate Meter

The Workbook assignments describe how to connect together the five black boxes shown in Fig. 10.7 to produce a pulse rate meter.

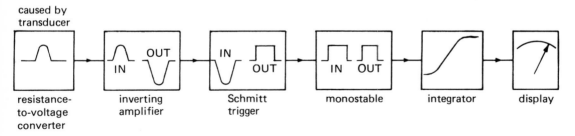

Fig. 10.7 The complete electronic system of the pulse rate meter

The whole system operates as follows.

1 The resistance-to-voltage converter uses a photocell to detect the small change in the amount of light transmitted through the flesh as the heart beats.
2 The inverting amplifier increases the size of the pulses produced by the resistance-to-voltage converter.
3 A Schmitt trigger 'sharpens' the pulses received from the amplifier, so that the monostable can be operated.
4 The monostable produces a regular set of pulses, all of equal height and width, but at the same frequency as the heart beats.
5 The integrator produces a steady voltage proportional to the heart beat rate, which is displayed on a moving coil meter.

Answers to Questions

1 80 pulses per minute or beats per minute.
2 A display, either in printed form or on an oscilloscope, of the shape of the electrical signals from the heart and brain respectively.
3 The resistance increases.

11 Measuring Strain

■ Stress and Strain

Some things are very **elastic** – they change shape very easily when forces act on them, and return to their original shape when the forces are removed. That is what happens to an elastic band, a car tyre, the strings of a tennis racket (Fig. 11.1) and so on.

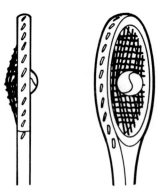

Fig. 11.1 Racket strings at moment of impact

You would be forgiven, however, for not believing that a spanner, or a pylon, or a ship's hull, change their shape under the effects of forces, but they do. The spanner bends slightly when it tightens a nut, the members of a pylon bend or twist or lengthen or shorten as the wind blows, and as a ship begins to move forward its hull gets shorter. The changes in shape are very small, of course, but they can be measured as you will see.

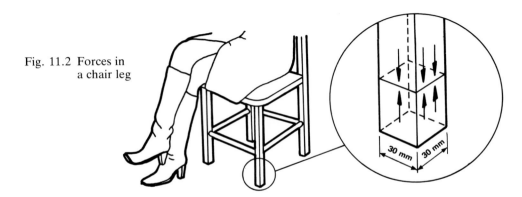

Fig. 11.2 Forces in a chair leg

In order to understand the meaning of stress and strain, let us look at the forces in a chair leg (Fig. 11.2). We shall assume that the seated person and the chair weigh 600 newtons (N) and that this weight is supported equally by the four legs. Thus the external force acting downwards on the top of one leg is 150 N. If the leg is, as we say, 'in equilibrium', the floor reacts to the 150 N force transmitted through the leg by providing an upward force on the leg of 150 N. (The floor actually distorts a little in order for this upward force to be produced.) Any cross-section of the chair leg is also in equilibrium, so equal and opposite forces of 150 N act across any section of the leg. The material the leg is made from is under mechanical stress, in this case **compressive stress**.

The kind of stress in a fishing line, which is being pulled tight by a fish you are about to land, is called **tensile stress**. Both compressive and tensile stress are measured by dividing the force acting across the section of material we are interested in, by the area of the section. Suppose the chair leg was square in cross-section, with dimensions 30 mm × 30 mm. Then the cross-sectional area of the leg is:

$$0.030 \times 0.030 \text{ m}^2 = 0.9 \times 10^{-3} \text{ m}^2.$$

So the compressive stress $= \dfrac{\text{force}}{\text{cross-sectional area}}$

$$= \frac{150}{0.9 \times 10^{-3}} = 167 \times 10^3 \text{ newtons/metre}^2$$

$$= 167 \times 10^3 \text{ N/m}^2.$$

1 A fish of weight 16 N dangles on the end of a fishing line of cross-sectional area 0.5 mm². What is the tensile stress in the line?

The chair leg shortens slightly (by an amount x) under the compressive force acting on it. We say the leg is experiencing 'mechanical strain', in this case **compressive strain** given by:

$$\text{compressive strain} = \frac{\text{change (reduction) in length}}{\text{original length}} = \frac{x}{l}$$

If the length l of the leg is 0.5 metres and $x = 0.1$ mm (so $x = 0.1 \times 10^{-3}$m), then

$$\text{compressive strain} = \frac{0.1 \times 10^{-3}\text{m}}{0.5 \text{ m}} = 2 \times 10^{-3}.$$

2 Why do compressive and tensile strains not have any units?

Tensile and compressive strains are not the only types of strain which are produced by forces. **Shear strain** occurs when a sideways force acts as shown in Fig. 11.3. In this case, the material tends to slide over itself. Similar to shear strain is the twisting of a bar held firm at one end and acted upon by a torque force at the other end, as Fig. 11.4 shows. The bending of the beams shown in Fig. 11.5 involves both tensile and compressive strains.

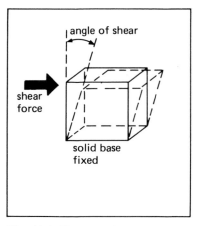

Fig. 11.3 Shear strain

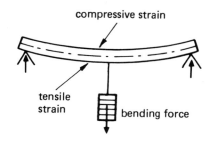

Fig. 11.4 Force causing torsion

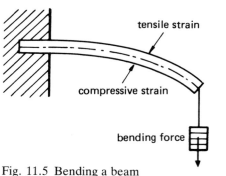

Fig. 11.5 Bending a beam
(a) Single cantilever

(b) Double cantilever

The designer of a structure needs to know a number of physical properties of the materials he uses. Two important properties are **Young's modulus** and the **elastic limit**.

If the chair leg of Fig. 11.2 is loaded to produce a gradually increasing stress and the corresponding strains measured, a graph of stress against strain would have the shape shown in Fig. 11.6. If the material behaves in an elastic manner over a certain range of values, a straight line would be obtained. The slope A/B is the **elastic modulus** of the wood. If we are dealing with changes of length, the ratio A/B is known as Young's modulus.

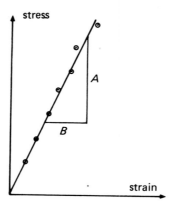

Fig. 11.6 Stress/strain graph

Young's modulus of elasticity for some common materials is shown in the table below.

Material	Young's Modulus N/m²
Copper	120×10^{12}
Wood (oak)	about 8×10^{12}
Steel	200×10^{12}
Glass	70×10^{12}
Aluminium	90×10^{12}

A material is said to be elastic if, on removing the forces which stress it, it returns to its original shape. If a material is stressed beyond the elastic limit it does not recover its original shape (see Fig. 11.7). Larger forces may cause the material to fracture.

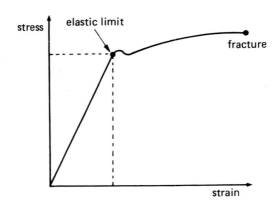

Fig. 11.7 Stress/strain graph

71

■ Why Measure Strain?

What is the point of knowing about stress and strain? Take the electricity pylon of Fig. 11.8 as an example of a structure which is under stress. An engineer will have designed the pylon to withstand all the forces it will experience in its long and lonely life; it has to stand not only its own weight but the effects of wind and ice, and the pulls of the cables it supports.

Fig. 11.8 An electricity pylon

Knowing Young's modulus of steel, the engineer will be able to predict, from an estimation of how large the various forces are on a member of the pylon, exactly what strain is produced (compressive/tensile) in each member. More important, the design should ensure that, even under the most adverse weather conditions, no member can fracture and weaken the pylon. Once a test pylon is built according to the designer's plans, instruments are used to test the type and magnitude of the strains in its members when the pylon is acted upon by various forces. The device which is attached to the pylon is the strain gauge.

■ What is a Strain Gauge?

In order to measure the small changes in shape caused by forces acting on rigid objects, a transducer called a **strain gauge** is used. A typical strain gauge is shown in Fig. 11.9, and consists of thin metal foil which is connected to an external circuit. It is made as follows.

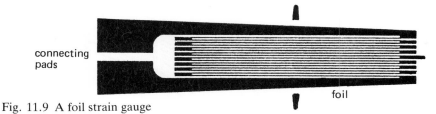

connecting
pads

foil

Fig. 11.9 A foil strain gauge

A thin foil is formed by rolling out an electrically resistive material, and cutting away parts by a photo etching process to leave the grid pattern as seen in Fig. 11.9. This produces a thin and flexible electrical resistor. How does it work?

The foil strain gauge is used by gluing it to the surface of the object which is being strained. As the object bends, expands or contracts, so does the gauge. Now if any metal conductor is stretched, its resistance increases and if it is compressed, its resistance decreases. In fact, the resistance of the conductor shown in Fig. 11.10, is directly proportional to its length l and inversely proportional to its area of cross-section A. Thus:

$$R \propto \frac{l}{A}$$

Stretching the conductor increases l and decreases A, thus increasing R.

conductor

area A

length l

Fig. 11.10 An electrical conductor

Fig. 11.11 Axes of a strain gauge

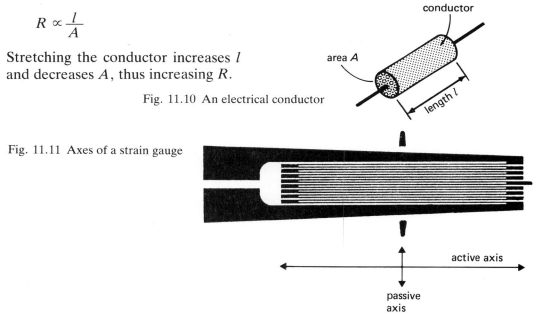

active axis

passive
axis

A strain gauge is said to have an **active axis** and a **passive axis** as shown in Fig. 11.11. As you might expect, a change of strain along the active axis

73

causes a greater change of resistance than the same strain along the passive axis. In use, the active axis is lined up with the direction in which the strain is to be measured. For example, if you wanted to measure the strain along the top surface of the single cantilever beam shown in Fig. 11.12, the foil strain gauge is glued to the surface of the cantilever as shown in Fig. 11.12.

Fig. 11.12 Positioning a strain gauge

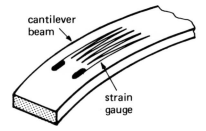

The resistance of most strain gauges is in the range 60 Ω to 2000 Ω, but the most common value is 120 Ω.

The **gauge factor**, G, of a strain gauge is the fractional change of resistance of the gauge, divided by the fractional change in the length of the gauge along the active axis.

$$G = \frac{r}{R} \bigg/ \frac{x}{l}$$

r is the change in resistance of the gauge of resistance R.
x is the change in length of the gauge of length l.

But $\frac{x}{l}$ is the strain e of the body to which the strain gauge is attached.

Therefore:

$$\frac{r}{R} = eG$$

which shows that the fractional change in resistance of the gauge is equal to the strain along the active axis multiplied by the gauge factor. For most gauges, the gauge factor has a value in the range 1.8 to 2.2.

If we know the gauge factor G (say 2.0), the strain (e) it undergoes (say 5×10^{-4}) and the resistance, R, of the strain gauge (say 120 Ω), we can work out the change in resistance of the gauge as follows:

$$\frac{r}{R} = eG$$

$$r = ReG = 120 \times 5 \times 10^{-4} \times 2.0$$

$$= 0.12 \ \Omega$$

Such a small change in resistance needs special circuitry to amplify it and display the strain on a meter.

■ The Wheatstone Bridge

In order to convert the small change in resistance of the gauge into a deflection on a meter, we shall need to use the instrumentation system shown in Fig. 11.13.

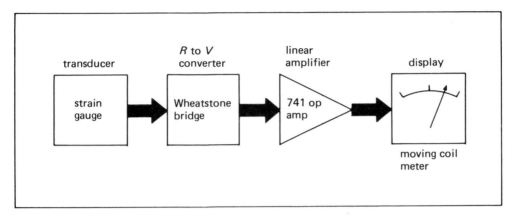

Fig. 11.13 The black box elements of the strain meter

A suitable resistance-to-voltage converter for a strain gauge is the Wheatstone bridge shown in Fig. 11.14. It consists of two voltage dividers R_1/R_2 and R_3/RG connected in parallel across a battery. Resistors R_1, R_2 and R_3 are chosen to be about equal to the resistance RG of the strain gauge. A voltmeter is connected between the join of R_1/R_2 and R_3/RG.

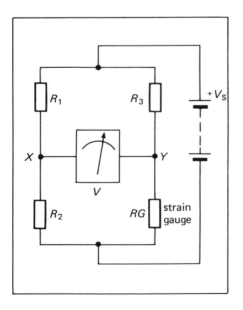

Fig. 11.14 Wheatstone bridge

If $R_1 = R_2$ and $R_3 = RG$, the voltages at points X and Y are equal so that voltmeter V does not measure a voltage. Suppose now strain gauge RG is attached to the surface of a material which is under tensile stress and experiencing tensile strain, so that its resistance increases slightly. The voltage at Y now rises, going slightly above that at X. The voltmeter now indicates a small difference of voltage between points X and Y, and the needle deflects to the right, say. If the strain gauge is attached to the surface of an object which is experiencing compressive strain, it shortens and its resistance decreases slightly. The voltage at Y falls below that at X and the deflection of the voltmeter needle is to the left.

The Wheatstone bridge is a circuit which converts resistance change into voltage change. But, since the resistance change of the strain gauge is very small, the voltage change is also very small and needs to be amplified using a 741 op amp as shown in Fig. 11.13.

By mathematically analysing the circuit for the single strain gauge, the change in output voltage V_{out} for a fractional change in resistance of the gauge (r/R) is given by:

$$V_{out} = \frac{V_s r}{4R}$$

to an accuracy of about 1%. Note two points about this equation.

1 The change in output voltage V_{out} is proportional to the change in resistance r of the gauge, and hence to the strain it is responding to.
2 The output voltage is proportional to the supply voltage V_s.

Thus, for small changes of strain, V_{out} is proportional to r and hence proportional to strain. This linear change of voltage with change of strain can be amplified by a linear amplifier like the 741 op amp to produce a linear deflection on a meter.

We know that $\frac{r}{R} = eG$, so

$$V_{out} = \frac{V_s eG}{4}$$

i.e. V_{out} is proportional to strain e.

As you will discover in Assignment 1 of Activity 11, you can construct a strain meter which will indicate whether the strain a body experiences is compressive or tensile.

□ **Temperature Effects**

A change of temperature affects the resistance of electrical conductors (remember the thermistor) and the metal foil of the strain gauge is no exception. An increase in temperature increases the resistance of the gauge so that this adds to the effect of tensile strain. Thus the output voltage V_{out} is higher than it should be if the temperature were constant.

Figure 11.15 shows a technique for compensating for the effects of temperature. A dummy gauge RG_1 is put in place of resistor R_3 (see Fig. 11.14). This gauge is placed close to the gauge RG which is undergoing strain but it is not itself strained. Its temperature is therefore the same as RG's temperature. It is possible to show mathematically that a change of temperature does not now affect the output voltage change produced by the Wheatstone bridge. In fact, now

$$V_{out} = \frac{V_s r}{2(2R+r)}$$

Because of the problem of ensuring that both the strained and unstrained gauges are at the same temperature, and the bother of having to produce an unstrained specimen of the material, it is usual to mount the dummy gauge on the same specimen as the measuring gauge, but with its active axis at right angles to the direction of strain as shown in Fig. 11.15b.

Fig. 11.15 The technique for temperature compensation
   (a) Use of a dummy gauge

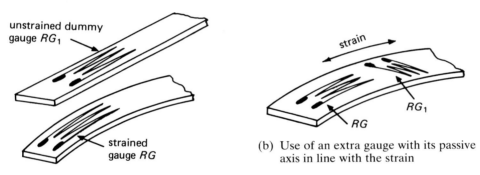

(b) Use of an extra gauge with its passive axis in line with the strain

Answers to Questions
1 32×10^6 N/m^2.
2 Because both 'change in length' and 'original length' are in the same units – in the example given in the text, metres (m).

12 Tachometers

■ Rotating Devices

This chapter is concerned with ways of measuring the rate at which mechanical devices rotate. After finding out what black boxes are required to make an instrument for measuring rate of rotation, you will build a **tachometer** and use this instrument to measure the rate of rotation of the shaft of an electric motor.

Why do we want to measure rate of rotation anyway? Modern machinery makes use of a large number of rotating parts. The engineer needs to know at what rate these parts rotate in order to predict how fast a car, for example, will go along a road, or how much power the engine will develop or whether rotation is so fast that there could be mechanical failure. How fast do you think a racing car can go before centrifugal forces tear the tyres off the rims of the wheels?

The bicycle is more humble than a racing car but it, too, makes use of devices which rotate (Fig. 12.1). The **wheels** propel the bike along the road and its **gears** enable the rider to make efficient use of the power produced.

1 Apart from the wheel on a car or bike, can you name three other mechanical devices which rotate?

Fig. 12.1 Racing bikes at speed, putting devices which rotate to good use

■ Frequency of Rotation

The rate or frequency of rotation of machinery is measured in **revolutions per minute (revs/min)**. This unit is the number of complete turns made in one minute plus any fraction of a turn in that time.

2 How many revolutions per minute are made by a long play record?
3 The spindle of an electric motor is rotating at 30 revs/second. What is this speed in revs/min?
4 A bicycle has wheels of diameter 0.6 m and is being ridden at 9 metres/second. What is the speed of rotation of the wheels in revs/min?
(Use the approximate value of π as 3 not 3.14.)

It is easy to measure the frequency of rotation of a wheel or axle which is rotating slowly. Making a mark on the wheel and counting the number of complete rotations in one minute would give you the answer.

But suppose the wheel is rotating so fast that you cannot count the regular position of the marker? The job must then be done automatically by a tachometer which will detect the marker every time it has completed one rotation. The signals received from the marker are then processed so the rate of rotation in revs/min can be displayed on a meter. A tachometer can be made from three black boxes. Each black box has a specific job to do, as shown in Fig. 12.2.

Fig. 12.2 Instrumentation
system of a
tachometer

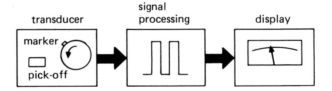

Let us have a look at each black box in turn, starting with the transducer black box.

■ Choosing a Transducer

The obvious way of detecting each revolution of a wheel is to put a cam on the spindle and use it to operate a mechanical switch (see Fig. 12.3) every time the spindle completes a revolution. This method works all right at low rates of revolution but is unreliable at high speeds.

Fig. 12.3 A mechanically operated switch

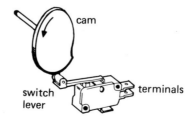

It is also noisy and likely to wear out quickly. If possible, it is better not to make contact with the wheel or axle. What is needed is a **proximity transducer** which senses the marker on the wheel without actually touching it. Two types of proximity transducer will be looked at in this chapter, one relying on **magnetism** and one on **light**.

■ Magnetic Transducer

A small magnet is fixed on a wheel or axle. Placed a short distance from it is a magnetically operated switch known as a **reed switch**. This switch is called the **pick-off** as it 'picks-off' the signal produced by the movement of the magnet (see Fig. 12.4).

Fig. 12.4 Reed switch

In the reed switch, there are two metal reeds which can be magnetised in an external magnetic field. By a process called 'magnetic induction', the external magnetic field induces magnetism in the metal reeds, causing the free end of one reed to have a north magnetic pole and the free end of the other reed, a south magnetic pole. As you probably know from your science lessons, unlike magnetic poles attract. Thus the free ends of the reeds draw together, so completing the circuit connected to the reed switch.

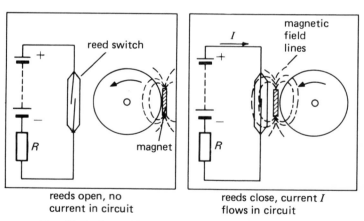

reeds open, no current in circuit   reeds close, current I flows in circuit

Fig. 12.5 The reed switch as a proximity transducer

Figure 12.5 shows the operation of the reed switch as a magnet attached to the wheel moves past it. For every revolution of the wheel, the reed switch operates briefly as the magnet sweeps past it. Surprisingly, reed switches are very fast-acting and the reeds will open and close reliably for speeds of up to 6000 revs/min. Assignment 2 in Activity 12 shows you how to use the reed switch to detect each revolution of a wheel.

■ Optical Transducer

In the **light-operated transducer** the marker on the wheel consists of a piece of reflective material like white paint, from which light reflects on to a light-sensitive pick-off every time the wheel rotates once. The light sensitive device which is used here is a **phototransistor**. A photocell could be used but it is not as fast-acting as the phototransistor and so would not respond for rapidly rotating wheels. Figure 12.6 shows the principle of using the phototransistor. The phototransistor pick-off is mounted close to the wheel so that light, reflected from the marker every time the wheel is in a certain position, is 'picked-off' by the phototransistor.

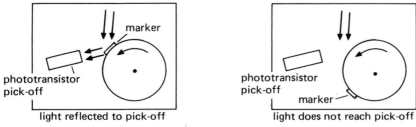

Fig. 12.6 The phototransistor as a proximity transducer

Compared with the reed switch pick-off, the phototransistor can respond very much faster so it can be used as a pick-off for very high speeds of revolution.

Assignment 3 in Activity 12 shows how the phototransistor requires to be connected up in order to provide a regular series of voltage pulses from the interruption of a light beam.

□ The Complete Tachometer Circuit

The circuit shown in Fig. 12.7 is that of an electronic tachometer which will be built in Assignment 5 of Activity 12.

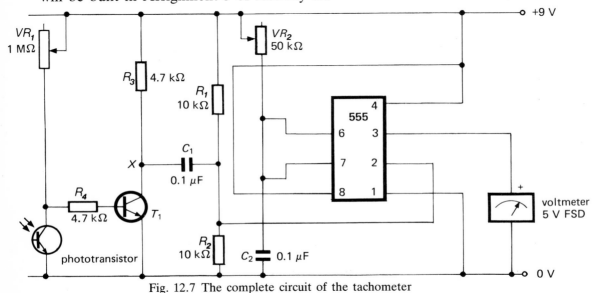

Fig. 12.7 The complete circuit of the tachometer

This simple circuit is based upon a phototransistor pick-off and a '555' type integrated circuit operating in the monostable mode as described in Chapter 3. The variable resistor VR_1 adjusts the sensitivity of the circuit so that it can be used under different lighting conditions. The transistor T_1 acts as a switch magnifying the small change in voltage across the phototransistor caused by it switching on and off as the light level changes. The changing voltage at point X is connected to the monostable circuit by the **coupling capacitor** C_1. The resistors R_1 and R_2 form a potential divider as described in Chapter 1 and set the level below which the monostable changes its state.

The monostable circuit is very similar to that described in Chapter 3 where the combination of VR_2 and C_2 form the time setting control, VR_2 adjusting the time for which the monostable circuit remains on. It is important that the time period of the monostable is less than the interval between successive pulses from the phototransistor or the circuit will try to re-trigger. The effect of adjusting VR_2 is shown in Assignment 4.

Answers to Questions
1 Drill, gear wheel, roundabout, turntable, windmill, etc.
2 $33\frac{1}{3}$ rpm.
3 1800 rpm.
4 300 rpm.

13 Weather Recording

■ Some Reminders

If you have completed all the earlier work in this course, you will now be familiar with the basic circuit designs for the following six electronic instruments: thermometer; light meter; sound intensity meter; strain meter; tachometer; pulse rate meter.

In assembling these circuits, you have seen how electronic instruments have certain features in common. Each instrument is made up from three basic building blocks (or black boxes) which have particular functions to perform. The instrumentation system of an electronic instrument consists of the following.

1 A transducer black box.
   The choice of transducer depends on the quantity to be measured.
2 A signal processor black box.
   The kind of signal processing depends on:
   (a) the characteristics of the electrical signal from the transducer;
   (b) the type of display method to be used.
3 A display black box.
   The display may be analogue (usually a moving coil meter) or digital (usually a seven-segment LCD or LED display).

1 Name a transducer for temperature measurement.
2 What kind of signal processing is required if pulses are to be 'averaged' on a moving coil meter so that the frequency of the pulses produces a deflection proportional to frequency?
3 What two kinds of digital display are in common use?

You have also seen how important it is to set down the specification of the instrument you intend to build. For example, a thermometer designed for measuring body temperature (a clinical thermometer) might have the following specification.

Quantity to be Measured	*Body Temperature*
Range	35°C to 42°C
Accuracy	±0.2°C
Output signal	0 to +3 V dc over specified range
Speed of response	30 seconds
Power supply	9 V dc battery operated
Display	digital

In addition, the temperature probe must not be toxic, i.e. react in any way with the body tissues. The probe must be comfortable when in position. You may be able to think of other desirable aspects of the design of a clinical thermometer.

■ Weather Station Instruments

In this section we shall be looking at some of the instruments you could include in a weather station.

Fig. 13.1 Simple anemometer for measuring wind speed.

Once you have evaluated the circuit design, you could make up a permanent assembly for inclusion in a weather station. What kind of instruments would you need in a weather station? Perhaps the most important ones are for measuring the following quantities in the ranges indicated.

Quantity to be Measured	Range	Accuracy	Speed of Response
Wind speed	0–30 m/s	±2 m/s	less than 5 seconds
Wind direction	360°	±22½°	less than 5 seconds
Atmospheric temperature	−15°C to 30°C	±1°C	less than 10 seconds
Atmospheric pressure	950–1050 mbar	±10 mbar	less than 30 seconds
Light intensity	50–5000 lux	±10% of full scale deflection	less than 5 seconds
Rainfall	0–50 mm per day	±0.5 mm per day	less than 30 seconds

For each of these quantities, you might first decide on the method of recording or displaying the measured quantity. This will determine the signal processing required and your choice of transducer. On the other hand, a particular transducer might largely determine the signal processing you use and the method of display. For example, wind speed could be measured using two kinds of transducer. You could use an optically or magnetically operated transducer as in the tachometer design of Chapter 12, or you might decide to use, say, a thermistor which is cooled by a greater or lesser amount as air flows past it. The first transducer will need to be followed by an electronic integrator as a signal processor if the wind speed is to be displayed on a moving coil meter. The second transducer will probably need some kind of amplifier as a signal processor in order to operate a moving coil meter.

The following notes are intended to help you design and build the instruments listed above. As you will see, you can incorporate many of the circuit design ideas you met in Chapters 1 to 12.

■ Power Supply

If a number of electronic instruments are to be designed and built for a weather station, it would be a good idea to operate all of them from a common power supply. 12 volt car batteries (perhaps kept fully charged from a wind powered generator?) would provide an adequate supply and would enable the station to be set up at a point remote from the mains power supply. If the station is to operate on the roof of a building, you could use a mains operated 12 V dc supply.

■ Wind Speed (Anemometer)

Figure 13.2 shows a possible design for an anemometer for measuring wind speed. The wind impinging on the cups causes the shaft to rotate. The problem is to convert the rotational speed of the shaft into a reading on a meter of wind speed in metres per second.

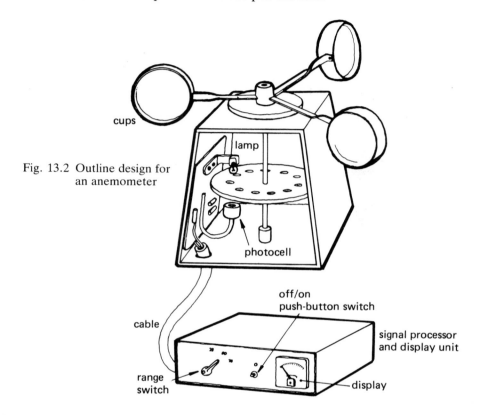

cups

Fig. 13.2 Outline design for an anemometer

lamp

photocell

off/on push-button switch

cable

signal processor and display unit

range switch

display

The ideas for the design of a tachometer, making use of optical or magnetic sensing of the rotation of the spindle, are described in Chapter 12. Figure 13.2 indicates an arrangement for optical sensing, and Fig. 13.3 the technique you might use for magnetic sensing.

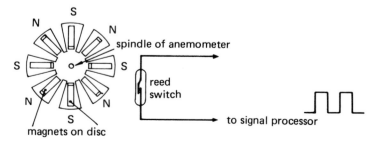

spindle of anemometer

reed switch

to signal processor

magnets on disc

Fig. 13.3 Small magnets attached to the anemometer shaft to operate a reed switch

Both types of non-contact sensing of the rotation of the anemometer spindle produce voltage pulses which must be processed before a reading can be obtained on a moving coil meter. You could use two kinds of signal processing: either make use of the 555 timer (as described in Chapter 3) to produce regular square wave pulses which the moving coil meter integrates to give a deflection proportional to rotational speed (and hence wind speed) of the shaft; or use the electronic integrator based on a 741 op amp as described in Chapter 4 and used in the pulse rate meter of Chapter 10.

An alternative method you might consider for measuring wind speed could be based on the use of strain gauges attached to the copper rod of the anemometer sketched in Fig. 13.4. The copper tube flexes as wind blows past the sphere and distorts the strain gauges. Provided the flexing is not too great the strain produced is proportional to a wind speed up to about 40 metres per second.

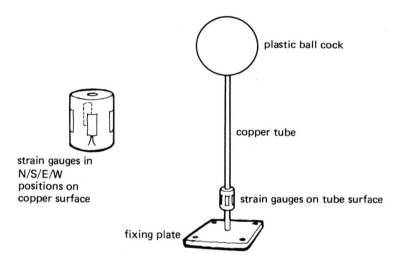

Fig. 13.4 An idea for using strain gauges in an anemometer design

The resistance change of the strain gauges can be sensed by a Wheatstone bridge whose output in turn is amplified by an op amp in order to operate a moving coil meter. The circuit design for this kind of signal processing was described in Chapter 11. A suitable circuit for making use of four strain gauges is shown in Fig. 13.5. Note that the strain gauges are operated as opposite pairs, NS and EW. This means that a westerly wind will cause an increase in the resistance of the west-facing gauge and a decrease in the resistance of the east-facing gauge.

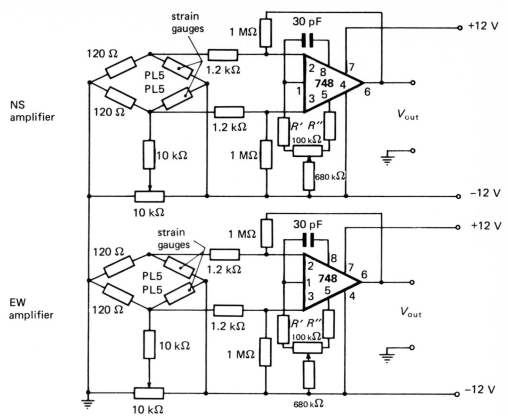

Fig. 13.5 Four strain gauges in a strain gauge amplifier

Note that the use of this design means that it is possible to obtain information about wind direction as well as wind speed but how to do this is left for you to sort out. Can you think of an advantage of this type of anemometer compared with the cup anemometer described previously?

■ Wind Direction (Wind Vane)

Although the circuit of Fig. 13.5 could give you information about wind speed as well as its direction, you might be interested in more direct methods for electronically measuring wind direction using a wind vane.

You will need to decide how you want to display the result. A moving coil meter could be calibrated so you would need an analogue output from the signal processor. A simpler solution might be to display the direction of the wind on a circular scale of sixteen points, illuminated lamps indicating the wind direction. Perhaps sixteen reed switches arranged at 360/16 = 22.5° intervals round the spindle of the wind vane as in Fig. 13.6?

Fig. 13.6 A simple design for a wind vane

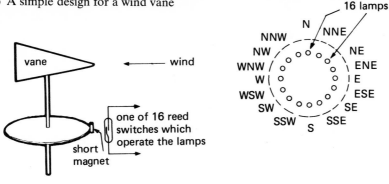

An alternative idea for an electronic wind vane could be based on the use of a photocell and light source, as shown in Fig. 13.7. A plastic cylinder is attached to the spindle of the vane and this is coated with an increasing depth of tint through 360°. As the cylinder rotates, the photocell receives increasingly more or less light with changes in wind direction. The photocell thus provides a signal which can be processed to produce a reading on a meter.

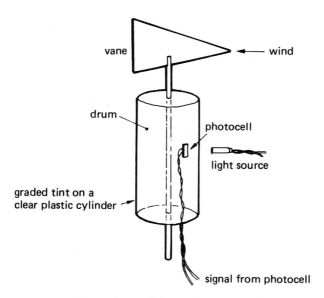

Fig. 13.7 A technique using a photocell in an electronic wind vane

Finally, a more sophisticated method of recording wind direction is illustrated by Fig. 13.8. This system makes use of coded tracks on a drum attached to the spindle of the vane. The coding is done by sticking opaque strips on the tracks so that the photocells (or phototransistors) are illuminated in a particular sequence as the drum rotates.

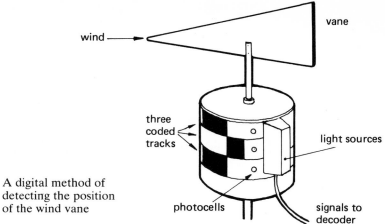

Fig. 13.8 A digital method of
detecting the position
of the wind vane

For example, the coding might be arranged so that eight points of the compass can be distinguished without ambiguity, that is each point provides a coded signal which cannot be confused with the signal from any other point. Using the binary code you met in Chapters 5 and 6, the three tracks could produce the eight binary signals $(000)_2$, $(001)_2$, $(010)_2$, $(011)_2$, $(100)_2$, $(101)_2$, $(110)_2$, $(111)_2$. To produce these signals is easy, but how do you decode them to give an analogue reading of wind direction on a moving coil meter? What we need is a digital-to-analogue converter. One way is to use the circuit in Fig. 13.9. A binary coded decimal (BCD) to decimal decoder (a TTL IC type 7442) decodes the three-bit signal from the coded strips on the anemometer drum to provide the output states as shown in the truth table.

Fig. 13.9 The connections to the 7442 BCD to decimal decoder

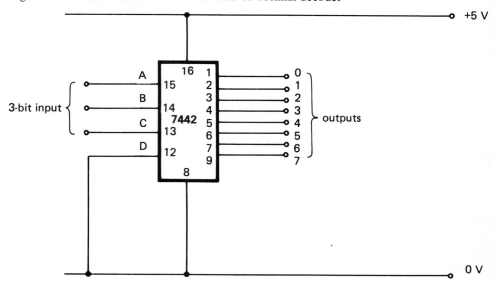

Decimal Number Equivalent	BCD Input				Output Logic States Pin Numbers							
	D	C	B	A	1	2	3	4	5	6	7	9
0	L	L	L	L	L	H	H	H	H	H	H	H
1	L	L	L	H	H	L	H	H	H	H	H	H
2	L	L	H	L	H	H	L	H	H	H	H	H
3	L	L	H	H	H	H	H	L	H	H	H	H
4	L	H	L	L	H	H	H	H	L	H	H	H
5	L	H	L	H	H	H	H	H	H	L	H	H
6	L	H	H	L	H	H	H	H	H	H	L	H
7	L	H	H	H	H	H	H	H	H	H	H	L

Notice that BCD input D is grounded and outputs 8 and 9 (pins 10 and 11 respectively) are unused, so that only eight logic output states are in use. Note also that all outputs are logic HIGH except the one corresponding to the decimal number equivalent of the BCD input which is at logic LOW. How do we now use these eight logic LOW outputs to give an analogue reading of wind direction on a meter?

Figure 13.10 is a simple digital-to-analogue converter which could be

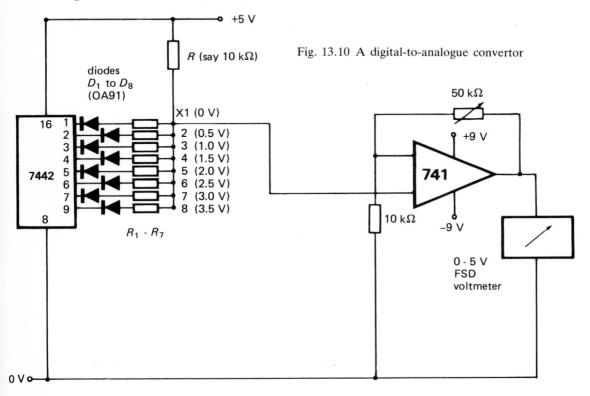

Fig. 13.10 A digital-to-analogue convertor

used. A 741 op amp is wired up as a non-inverting amplifier whose gain can be adjusted by means of the 50 kΩ variable resistor, so enabling the output voltage to be adjusted to correspond to an FSD of, say, 5 V. Voltage dividers are used to adjust each of the eight logic states to an appropriate fraction of the logic output voltage.

Suppose pin 4 of the 7442 goes logic LOW. Current then flows through R and R_4 into pin 4 and the voltage at X falls to a value determined by the values of R and R_4. The resistor values are chosen to give equal increments of voltage. These are fed into the 741 operational amplifier which is connected as a high input impedance low-gain amplifier to buffer the outputs of the 7442 from the low impedance voltmeter. Resistor values R and R_1 to R_7 are chosen to given equal increments of voltage over eight points. Note that the calculations for R_1 to R_7 ignore the voltage drop across each of the diodes, which is about 0.2 V. However, the pin 1 and 5 connections on the op amp can be used to 'zero' the output from the op amp when all the binary inputs are logic LOW.

Sample calculations of resistor values are given below.

$$\frac{R_1}{R_1 + R} = \frac{0.5 \text{ V}}{5 \text{ V}} = \frac{1}{10} \qquad\qquad \frac{R_5}{R_5 + R} = \frac{2.5 \text{ V}}{5.0 \text{ V}} = \frac{1}{2}$$

$$10R_1 = R_1 + R \qquad\qquad\qquad 2R_5 = R_5 + R$$

$$9R_1 = R = 10 \text{ k}\Omega \qquad\qquad\quad R_5 = R = 10 \text{ k}\Omega$$

$$R_1 = \frac{10 \text{ k}\Omega}{9} = 1.1 \text{ k}\Omega$$

■ Atmospheric Temperature

The basic circuit ideas for an analogue thermometer suitable for measuring temperature of the air in the range $-15°C$ to $40°C$ were described in Chapter 9. This instrument has the advantage that temperature can be recorded at some distance from the point of measurement. Thus the temperature probe can be outdoors but the actual electronic instrument can be indoors and protected from the weather. Of course, this is largely true of the other electronic instruments in your weather station.

■ Atmospheric Pressure

You may know the principles of operation of the two common types of mechanical barometer: the aneroid and Fortin types. The first depends upon the change in shape of an evacuated (airless) chamber and the second, on the change in levels of liquid (usually mercury) in a tube closed at the top and open at the bottom immersed in the liquid. You should check the operation of these two barometers by looking in a physics textbook.

Unless you make a water-filled Fortin-type barometer (which would be very long – why?), you are advised not to try modifying the mercury type to operate electronically, for they are costly instruments and, anyway, mercury is a toxic material. It is relatively easy to modify an aneroid barometer so that it gives an electronic readout. Alternatively, you could obtain a stack of evacuated capsules as shown in Fig. 13.11. About eight of these capsules will be required since the change in height due to atmospheric pressure changes is very small. How do you convert the changes in height of the capsules into an electrical signal which can be converted into a reading on a meter? One type of displacement transducer which you might try is shown in Fig. 13.11.

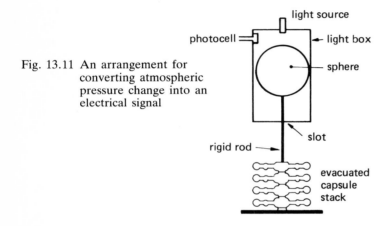

Fig. 13.11 An arrangement for converting atmospheric pressure change into an electrical signal

The sphere, e.g. a table tennis ball blackened except for an area near the top, moves up and down on the top of the rod as the air pressure changes. This causes more or less light to be reflected to the photocell, so providing an electrical signal which can be processed using ideas already discussed in Chapter 2.

Should you consider modifying an aneroid barometer, perhaps you could replace the pointer by a wheel, round which thread passes carrying a sphere in an arrangement similar to that of Fig. 13.11. Of course, an optical method of detecting the movement of the rod is not the only method you might use: changes of inductance and capacitance are two alternatives you might consider. You might also consider a strain gauge attached to the evacuated capsules.

■ **Light Intensity**

Circuit ideas for measuring light intensity, that is the intensity of daylight and artificial light, were discussed in Chapter 7. However, if you merely want to record the hours of sunshine received daily at a certain location, this is rather a different problem from actually measuring the intensity of daylight. You might think that it is an easier problem to solve? A transducer which actually responds to direct sunlight, not hazy sun through clouds, is required. The response of the transducer must then be converted to a reading on an analogue or digital meter.

A transducer which would respond to direct sunlight could be made from four photodiodes, photocells or phototransistors in a Wheatstone bridge arrangement (Fig. 13.12). Hazy, scattered sunlight would illuminate all photosensitive devices equally and provide no voltage difference between points X and Y, so the output voltage from the op amp is zero and the relay controlling a clock would not be energised. The photocells must be arranged so that if the sun shines on one of them, or certain combinations of them, a difference of voltage across points X and Y will occur and so gives an output voltage from the op amp which energises the relay. Resistors R_1 must be equal in value and should be adjusted to control the sensitivity of the circuit.

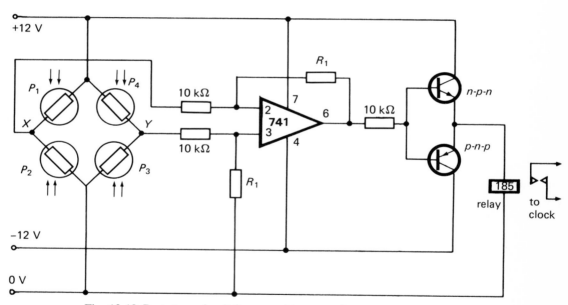

Fig. 13.12 Prototype circuit for a sunshine recorder

Is there a suitable arrangement of the photocell to 'look' at the skies which will allow only direct sunlight from any direction (roughly east-west) to energise the relay and so start a clock? What kind of clock would you use? Cheap, portable digital clock modules are now available in prebuilt form or easily built kits but you might consider constructing a drum recorder, clockwork or electric driven, on which a pen marks the passage of time.

■ Rainfall

One possibility for detecting whether rain has fallen is shown in Fig. 13.13. The transducer consists of two strain gauges mounted on opposite sides of a cantilever. Bending of the beam, caused by collected rain, causes the gauges to be strained.

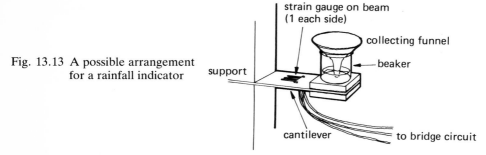

Fig. 13.13 A possible arrangement for a rainfall indicator

Before building the circuit required to process the signal from the Wheatstone bridge in which the strain gauges are to be connected, you will need to find out what quantity of rain will be collected in the container for a maximum daily rainfall of, say 5 mm. This will of course, depend on the cross-sectional area of the collecting funnel. The output voltage from the bridge circuit shown in Fig. 13.14 can be measured using a voltmeter when the beaker contains the maximum daily amount of rain. The amplifier will now need to have a voltage gain sufficient to provide, say, a maximum output voltage of 5 V. You will need finally to calibrate the meter deflection in millimetres of rainfall. Is the response of the meter linear? It should be, provided the bending of the beam is not too large.

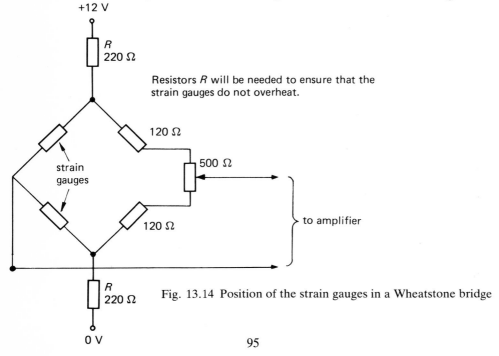

Fig. 13.14 Position of the strain gauges in a Wheatstone bridge

An alternative rainfall gauge could be made based on a balance type of arrangement, shown in Fig. 13.15. As the collecting bottle fills with water, the beam tilts and causes a decreasing amount of light to reach the photocell. The light box is similar to that used for the barometer transducer shown in Fig. 13.11.

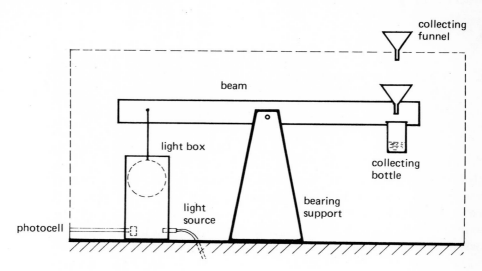

Fig. 13.15 An alternative rainfall gauge

Answers to Questions
1 Thermocouple, thermistor, *p-n* junction.
2 An electronic integrator.
3 Seven-segment LED and seven-segment LCD.